DATE DUE

APR 20			
MAY 10			
APR 2 0			
DEC 0 6 '10			

NUMBERS AT WORK
The Story and Science of Statistics

NUMBERS AT WORK
The Story and Science of Statistics

BLAIRSVILLE SENIOR HIGH SCHOOL
BLAIRSVILLE. PENNA.

HYMAN ALTERMAN

*Illustrated with charts and graphs by F. W. Taylor
and with photographs*

HARCOURT, BRACE & WORLD, INC.   NEW YORK

I wish to thank Abraham J. Berman, colleague and friend, for reading the manuscript and offering many helpful suggestions. Needless to say, any errors are the author's.

This book is for Tony, Ian, and Eric who are young and for Ina who is also young

CONTENTS

INTRODUCTION

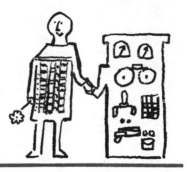

ON THE DAY you were born, you were probably the world's most beautiful baby to the adoring eyes of your parents. But many people outside your family circle were also interested in your arrival. To them, however, you were represented by a punch card similar to the one on the next page.

The instant you were born you became a statistic. Before you and your mother were out of the hospital, everything about you and your parents had been recorded on a punch card. Soon you were sailing through a sorter, counted on a calculator, compared on a collator, and whisked through a computer at dizzying speeds. You were swimming in a sea of statistics.

Here are some of the important questions you helped to answer:

1. The characteristics of babies born that year—their weight, their size, their sex, their health, the month of their birth, the very hour.

2. The proportions of white, Negro, Indian, and all other kinds of babies.

3. The age of mothers giving birth to their first, their second, or whatever number baby you were in your family.

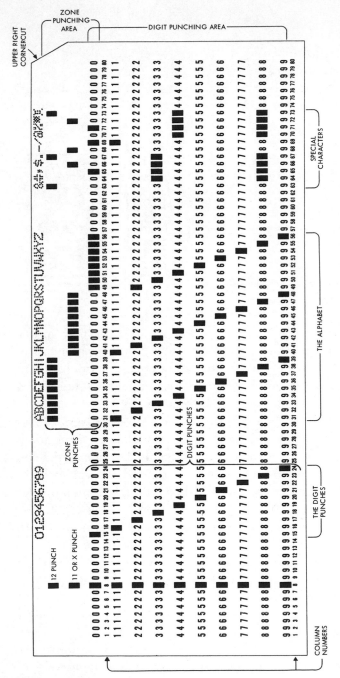

A punch card has space for 80 columns and 12 rows of information. Above the zero there is space for two more rows, if needed. Numeric and alphabetic symbols can be punched. Each letter has a numeric equivalent. When a card is passed through a sorter or reader, the punched (empty) holes are "sensed" by electrical contacts and information is recorded or stored. (IBM).

4. The ups and downs (the trend) of population in your city, your state, your country.

This list could go on and on to fill several pages. In a small way, you helped to tip the scales, reverse a trend, change an average, maintain a lead, or do any of the many things that a child's birth does in this vast world of statistics.

As you go through life, the number of punch cards prepared for you will grow and grow. In the ripeness of your old age, if all of them could be assembled, the thousands and thousands of holes in them would outline the story of your life.

Let us look at some of the occasions when people unknown to you will prepare a statistical summary about you and perpetuate it in a punch card. Your first card has already been recorded. Then:

You enter your father's income-tax return.

If your mother visits a baby clinic, a punch card will follow. With every visit it is added to, revised, or punched again.

When you enter kindergarten—and for every year of schooling as long as it lasts.

Whenever you take a test—city-wide, state-wide, or national.

Whenever you get a license—professional, driver's, or plumber's.

When you get your first traffic ticket—and for every ticket thereafter.

With your Social Security card.

When you open a bank account—savings or checking.

When the census taker counts you.

With your first job, if your company is a fair-sized one.

When you fill out your own income-tax return.

When you get married.

When you and your spouse start a new cycle in motion with your first baby.

The stack of cards grows and grows until the "deck" is completed when we die.

Why are all these records kept? Why are they studied? Why

is it important to know whether you are a boy or a girl or how old your mother was when you were born? Why, you may ask, is statistics so important?

Today, in our complicated world, no important decision is made without deep study of thousands, or even millions, of individual records. Look at the nature of the decisions made today after detailed statistical study.

In government: The future construction of schools and colleges. (Your birth played a part.)
The change in tax laws.
The change in minimum-wage laws.

In business: The expansion of industry; the future need for workers and professionals. (Your mother's age when you were born was important. It helped to indicate how fast the population was growing.)
The development of any new product. (The compact car was placed on the market only after a long statistical survey.)

In medicine: The effectiveness of polio vaccine was proved by statistical analysis.
Clues to the cause of some forms of cancer were the result of statistical analysis.
The safety and usefulness of most new drugs are tested statistically.

In science: Many examples will be shown in the section on graphs (Chapter 1).

In politics: The speeches that candidates for almost any public office, including that of President of the United States, make are often determined by statistical studies of voter interest.

The list could go on and on, but, as it is, it should give you some idea why records are gathered and studied.

This world of statistics will not, however, always remain something apart from you. The chances are excellent that at some time in your life you will have to work with and understand statistical material or statistical results. With the tremendous growth in the use of giant computers, the likelihood has increased. The list of occupations and professions to which a knowledge of statistics is essential is a long and growing one.

Even if you become a theoretical atomic physicist, you will not be able to function properly without it. The great Nobel Prize physicist, Werner Heisenberg, who has explored the world of particles within the atom, has said, "We see that the statistical nature of the laws of microscopic physics cannot be avoided. . . ."

Every rocket whirling around in space sends back a flood of statistical material, often directly into giant computers. Every spaceman sends back and returns with a huge mass of statistical information. Today, even before we have built a spaceship for a trip to the moon, vast amounts of statistical material are being collected and analyzed for the trip some spaceman will make. This must be done to protect him and to avoid danger to the spaceship. For example, the paths of meteors and meteorites must now be charted to check the probability (a term we will examine later) of their crossing the spaceship's path.

You might, of course, become a statistician. In that case, you will never be away from statistics.

What exactly does a statistician do? What is the function of statistics? We could put it this way: The function of a statistician, of statistics, is to make complicated information simple and understandable.

1 THE FREQUENCY DISTRIBUTION AND ITS USES: TABLES AND GRAPHS

IN FRANCE, in Spain, and in other parts of the world, fascinating paintings have been discovered in caves. Some of the paintings are of hunting scenes. Others are religious in nature. The paintings were made thousands of years ago by primitive man. They are often colorful and give proof of a high level of artistic ability.

If primitive man was a capable painter, it may not be too farfetched to imagine that he may also have been a statistician. Perhaps he kept records by scratching marks on the walls of his cave. He may have counted the number of rainy days during a season. Perhaps he kept some record of the number of animals he had killed. Alongside a painting of the animal, he might have shown the results of his hunting skill in this way:

Buffalo	//////////
Deer	////////
Tiger	//

Had he kept his records for two years, or two seasons, the result could have been the following statistical table:

Animals killed	50,001 B.C.		50,000 B.C.	
Total of all animals	///// ///// ///// /	(16)	///// ///// ///// /////	(20)
Buffalo	///// ///	(8)	///// /////	(10)
Deer	////	(4)	///// ///	(8)
Tiger	////	(4)	//	(2)

He could have spent the cold winter months in his cave drawing many conclusions from this simple table. At once, he would see that his total "catch" had increased by 25 percent:

$$\frac{20 - 16}{16} \times 100 = \frac{4}{16} \times 100 = \frac{400}{16} = 25 \text{ percent}$$

(In the numerator, subtract the total number of animals in the earlier year from the total number in the later year. The denominator is the total number in the earlier year. Multiply the fraction by 100 to obtain the percent.)

In the same way, he could have calculated that his "bag" of deer had doubled but that he had killed only 50 percent, or half, of the number of tigers he had killed the year before.

The above account is, of course, completely fanciful. We know nothing about the statistical ability of primitive man. However, as society developed and became more complicated, men began to keep records and then to analyze them. By the fourteenth and fifteenth centuries, Venice and Florence, two of the wealthiest and most powerful of the Italian city-states at that time, were already keeping complicated statistical records. From their records, we know that in 1423, in Venice, 16,000 men were working in the shipbuilding industry. There were 1,000 nobles with yearly incomes ranging from 70 to 4,000 ducats. The yearly trade of the city amounted to 10,000,000 ducats. This brought a yearly profit of 4,000,000 ducats.

In Florence, record-keeping started even earlier. It included more information and was more methodical. In 1338, the population of the city was estimated to be 90,000. The estimate was based on the sale of bread, of which records were kept. Six thousand children were baptized that year. These included 300 to 500 more boys than girls. Records were kept of the amount of money in circulation; of state income and spending; of the value and type of trade; of the kinds of businesses in existence. Most records were revised by means of a recount every ten years.

The statistics we have mentioned are elementary. They consisted mostly of counting. But even counting, on a large scale, as we shall see later, is not a simple matter. For example, we do not know how many people were really unemployed in this country during the great depression of the 1930's. And this was less than thirty years ago!

In statistics, one of the first steps is usually to count, to gather numbers, or observations, as they are frequently called. The next step is to put the numbers into some kind of order. And the simplest way to put numbers in order is in the form of a *frequency distribution.*

How to Make a Frequency Distribution

Let us examine a real situation.

One day, in class, the teacher asks the students this question. "Will each of you please tell me how many hours you spent watching television last week?" As the 25 students call out their answers to the question, the teacher writes the numbers on the blackboard. These are the numbers called out:

10, 7, 12, 10, 3, 6, 10, 10, 12, 18, 0, 10, 21, 7, 10, 10, 6, 7, 12, 12, 7, 10, 18, 12, 10

As the numbers were called out, they would make no sense. Even as written on the blackboard, they still look like a meaningless scramble. Had the teacher written them in five columns of five numbers each, this is how they would appear:

10	6	0	10	7
7	10	10	6	10
12	10	21	7	18
10	12	7	12	12
3	18	10	12	10

They now look like a puzzle or a problem in arithmetic.

Let us proceed to make some order out of the numbers.

1. From lowest to highest (0 to 21), enter every number, no matter how often it appears, only once. This is the result:

0, 3, 6, 7, 10, 12, 18, 21

2. List these numbers in a column on the left-hand side. Then, make a mark (/) next to the number as often as it appears on the blackboard. This is the result:

Number of hours spent watching TV during a week	Number of students	Total
0	/	1
3	/	1
6	//	2
7	////	4
10	///// ////	9
12	/////	5
18	//	2
21	/	1
		25

This record of the frequencies (how often every number of hours was called out) can now be shown in the form of a simple statistical table:

Number of hours spent watching TV during a week	Number of students
0	1
3	1
6	2
7	4
10	9
12	5
18	2
21	1
	25

An important statistical operation is now complete. Complicated information has been simplified.

How to use the table

Now that the information is tabulated (to tabulate means "to make into the form of a table"), what can we learn from it? Let's ask some questions.

1. What percent of the students spent less than 10 hours during the week watching TV?

the number watching
less than 10 hours $\rightarrow \dfrac{8}{25} \times 100 = \dfrac{800}{25} = 32$ percent

2. What percent spent exactly 10 hours?

$\dfrac{9}{25} \times 100 = \dfrac{900}{25} = 36$ percent

3. What percent spent more than 10 hours?

the number watching
12 to 21 hours $\rightarrow \dfrac{8}{25} \times 100 = \dfrac{800}{25} = 32$ percent

From the answers obtained above, it is now possible to make a more advanced statistical table:

Number of hours spent watching TV during a week	Percent of students
Less than 10	32
10	36
More than 10	32
	100

Number of students: 25

It is possible to reach many other conclusions from the original table, page 17. On the basis of the table, one can say that 1 of every 5 students (5 out of 25) probably spent 2 hours per day during 6 days of the week (a total of 12 hours) watching TV.

The method described above, simple as it may seem, is probably more widely used than any other form of statistics. This method is used by banks, insurance companies, and many other large organizations to describe their work or business. It is also used by all branches of government in their reports. It shows the results of their very complicated counting in a simple, understandable way.

Changing Numbers into Pictures

You may have heard the expression, "One picture is worth a thousand words." Nobody believes this more strongly than statisticians. They have spent a great deal of time, thought, and energy in developing ways to show the results of their work in the form of simple pictures. Why? There are several reasons.

1. Some people are afraid of numbers.
2. Some people don't understand them.
3. Some people don't have time to read them.
4. Statisticians want their work to be easily available.

Using our TV tables, let us examine the most common ways to present these results in picture form.

The simple graph

This is the oldest but still the most widely used method of illustrating statistical results. It appears often in newspapers, in financial reports, in advertising, and in many, many magazine cartoons.

In plotting (designing and making) the graph, the number of hours spent watching TV is shown on the horizontal line, the X-axis. The number of students, or frequency, is shown on the vertical axis, the Y-axis. Statisticians and mathematicians all over the world use these terms. Anyone designing a graph uses this scheme.

The number of hours is called the "independent" variable because the hours go on and on in a regular order. The number of students, however, "depends upon" the number of hours we are talking about. Thus the frequency is the "dependent" variable.

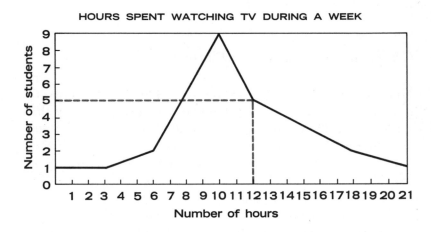

Reading the graph

The broken line on the graph will help explain how to read it. Let us suppose that we want to know how many students spent 12 hours watching TV. These are the steps to follow:

1. Find 12 hours on the horizontal axis.

2. Go upward in a straight (perpendicular) line until the line of the graph itself is reached (in this illustration, the fifth line above the X-axis).

3. At the point of contact, follow a horizontal line to the number of students.

Our line brings us to the number 5. Therefore, we can say that 5 students spent 12 hours during the week watching TV. By going back to the original table, page 17, we see that this is really so.

Mickey Mantle's career—in pictures

Because this idea of X and Y is important, it is worth examining in another situation. Imagine that you want to make a graph of the number of home runs hit by Mickey Mantle in every season of his career. Since the years proceed in regular order and are "independent" of the number of Mickey Mantle's home runs, they should be shown on the horizontal line, or X-axis. The number of home runs is the dependent variable and should be shown on the Y-axis. The number of home runs "depends upon" the year selected.

Notice that the X-axis can be extended to show future years. It is reasonable to assume that Mickey Mantle will be hitting home runs for some years to come.

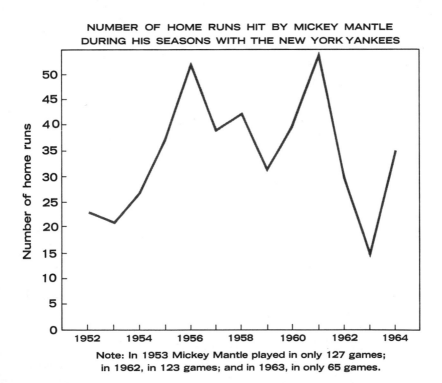

NUMBER OF HOME RUNS HIT BY MICKEY MANTLE
DURING HIS SEASONS WITH THE NEW YORK YANKEES

Note: In 1953 Mickey Mantle played in only 127 games;
in 1962, in 123 games; and in 1963, in only 65 games.

PROBLEM 1: *In which year did Mickey Mantle hit the most home runs? How many did he hit that year?*
PROBLEM 2: *How many home runs did he hit in 1960?*

(Answers to all problems appear in the Answer Section at the back of the book.)

Below and on the next page are two line graphs of rather complicated scientific findings. From what you now know about line graphs, you may be able to interpret some of the information.

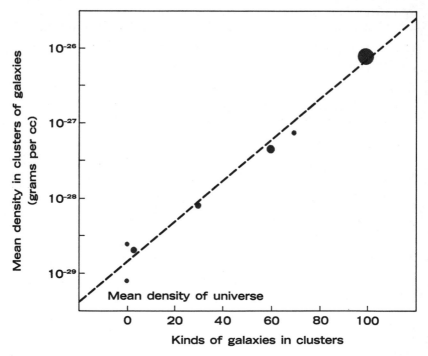

Line graph shows an astronomer's hypothesis that the kinds of galaxies tend to change from spiral to elliptical and disk shapes as mean (average) density increases.

$(10^{-29} = \frac{1}{10^{29}}; 10^{29}$ *is the same as 1 followed by 29 zeros.)*

(Halton C. Arp, "The Evolution of Galaxies," Scientific American, January 1963, p. 76)

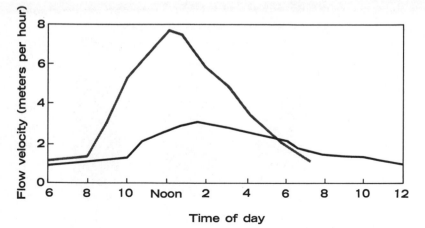

Movement of sap in twigs (light line) and trunk (dark line) of trees is related to the time of day. The physiologist shows that sap rises and settles earlier in twigs than in the trunk. (Martin H. Zimmerman, "How Sap Moves in Trees," Scientific American, March 1963, p. 136)

The bar graph

A bar graph is probably the second most common way to show the results of statistical work. It is useful for several reasons.

1. It is easier to make than a line graph.
2. It is easier to read and understand.
3. There may not be enough information for a line graph.
4. Some comparisons look better on a bar graph.
5. A report filled only with line graphs could become boring.

At the top of page 24 is a bar graph showing the information in the table on page 17. Since the table has only three units of information, a bar graph will be much more suitable than a line graph.

You may get some idea how a simple bar graph is used in scientific investigation from a study of the bar graph on page 25, prepared by Norman D. Newell, Curator of the Department of Fossil Invertebrates, American Museum of Natural History in New York City. It is based on a study by Jim J. Hester of the Museum of New Mexico of Santa Fe. It shows how many years

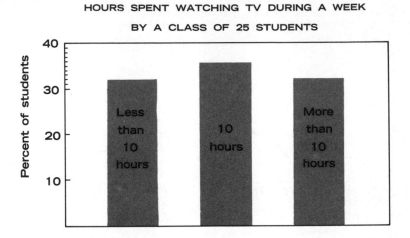

HOURS SPENT WATCHING TV DURING A WEEK
BY A CLASS OF 25 STUDENTS

before the present time certain large North American animals disappeared from the earth.

Bar graphs for comparisons

A bar graph helps us make comparisons.

Imagine that our TV information was obtained from a class of 25 boys. Another teacher asked the same question in a class of 25 girls. We shall compare the results in another bar graph.

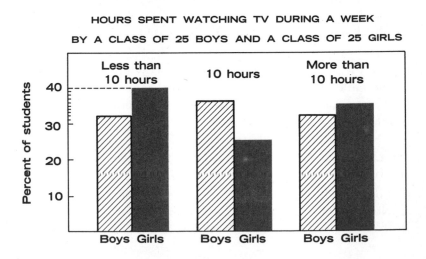

HOURS SPENT WATCHING TV DURING A WEEK
BY A CLASS OF 25 BOYS AND A CLASS OF 25 GIRLS

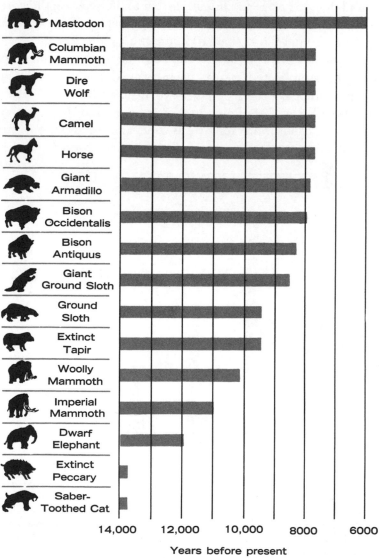

TIME OF EXTINCTION OF CERTAIN LARGE
NORTH AMERICAN ICE-AGE ANIMALS

Mastodon
Columbian Mammoth
Dire Wolf
Camel
Horse
Giant Armadillo
Bison Occidentalis
Bison Antiquus
Giant Ground Sloth
Ground Sloth
Extinct Tapir
Woolly Mammoth
Imperial Mammoth
Dwarf Elephant
Extinct Peccary
Saber-Toothed Cat

14,000   12,000   10,000   8000   6000

Years before present

*A paleontologist's simple bar graph indicates the time when certain mammals that once roamed North America disappeared.
(Norman D. Newell, "Crises in the History of Life," Scientific American, February 1963, p. 88)*

To find the value that any bar represents, or stands for, extend the top horizontal line of the bar to the scale on the vertical axis. This has been done on the comparison bar graph for girls watching TV less than 10 hours during the week.

Again from the field of science, a comparison bar graph sums up complicated results of an experiment in physiology and psychology. Professor Jay Boyd Best of the University of Illinois College of Medicine used this method to show some of the results of his work relating hunger and environment (surroundings) in the feeding time of planarians (worms).

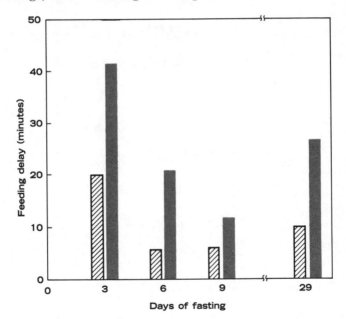

Bar graph shows a biophysicist's experimental results. Planarians (worms) took food sooner in familiar surroundings (striped bars) than in unfamiliar (solid bars). The aim was to see if they remembered surroundings. They would be apt to feed sooner if they did. (Jay Boyd Best, "Protopsychology," Scientific American, *February 1963, p. 60)*

A pie that's not for eating

When you order pie in a restaurant, all the pieces are approximately equal in size. However, sometimes a pie is sliced unequally. At home, Father probably receives the largest slice of pie. Mother's piece may depend upon her diet. Younger sisters and brothers probably receive less than you do.

Based upon the idea of a pie divided unequally, a third method of illustrating statistical results is called the *pie chart* or *circle graph*. The principal reason for the use of a pie chart or circle graph is to show how all of something is divided into parts of various sizes. It shows the relationship among the parts of the whole. It is also used when the data would not look attractive on a bar graph or would be more difficult to interpret.

A pie is, of course, a circle with 360 degrees. (A degree is expressed by the symbol °.) This, as you may know, is true of all circles, large or small. How many of the 360 degrees each piece of information will get (how large a slice of the pie) depends upon how large it is in comparison with all the other pieces of information that will share the pie.

The important facts to remember about a pie chart are:

1. The whole pie represents 100 percent, or everything we are examining.

2. Each slice of pie, each portion or share, is part of 100 percent or one part of the whole.

Let us plan a pie chart from the results in the table on page 18. This is the information we have:

1. Thirty-two percent of the students spent less than 10 hours.

2. Thirty-six percent spent exactly 10 hours.

3. Thirty-two percent spent more than 10 hours.

The pie, therefore, has to be divided into three pieces. To put it another way, 100 percent ($32 + 36 + 32$) has to be divided into the 360 degrees of the circle. This is the way the calculations are made:

$$\frac{\text{the first percent}}{\text{the total percent}} \rightarrow \frac{32}{100} \times 360° = \frac{11{,}520}{100} = 115° \text{ (approx.)}$$

$$\frac{\text{the second percent}}{\text{the total percent}} \rightarrow \frac{36}{100} \times 360° = \frac{12{,}960}{100} = 130° \text{ (approx.)}$$

HOURS SPENT WATCHING TV DURING A WEEK:

PROPORTIONS IN A CLASS OF 25 STUDENTS

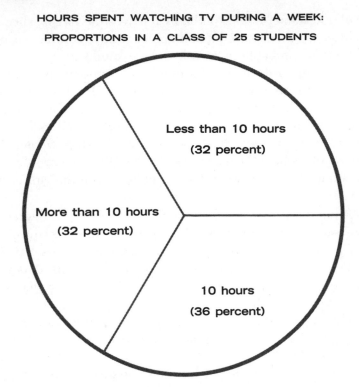

The third share is the same as the first, since it is also 32 percent. It, too, will be represented on the circle, or pie, by 115
degrees. The pie will have three slices, measuring: 1. 115°,
2. 130°, and 3. 115°.

For the information of the American people, the division of
one of the largest pies in the world is shown in just this way.
In January of each year, the President sends to the Congress a
budget request. This is a request for the amount of money that
will be needed to run the business of the government. The day
after he sends it, practically every newspaper in the country
prints a pie chart. It shows where the money will come from
and how it will be spent—how this huge pie will be divided.

On page 29 is a copy of the pie chart of the 1966 fiscal year
(the fiscal, or business, year is from July 1, 1965, to June 30,

THE BUDGET DOLLAR

Fiscal year 1966 estimates

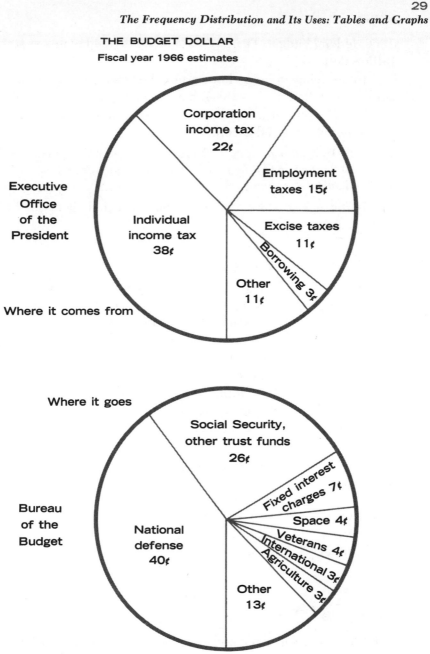

1966) federal budget. The pie that will be divided is almost 100 billion dollars!

In studying the pie chart, remember that each pie represents one dollar. This is the same as making it represent 100 percent. Do you see why? If not, it is explained in the answers to Problems 1 and 2 that follow.

PROBLEM 1: *What percent of the budget will be spent for agriculture?*
PROBLEM 2: *How many degrees of the circle (approximately) does national defense account for?*

If the answers are not clear, you can find them in the Answer Section.

The pictorial chart or pictogram

The winner of the beauty prize among the various ways of showing statistical results is the pictorial chart. It is also the baby of the family. You may have seen such charts in newspapers, magazines, or books. Sometimes the chart shows rows of men, with the explanation, "Each man represents 1 million workers." Or it may show rows of small railroad cars filled with coal and say, "Each car represents 1 million tons of coal."

Such charts are usually used in the following situations:

1. When the need to attract the reader's attention is great.

2. When a very large audience will see it.

3. When a quick impression rather than careful study is the goal.

4. When the information does not have to be too exact.

If we wanted every student in the high schools of our city to see the results of our TV study, we might prepare from the table on page 17 the kind of pictorial chart you see on the next page.

Summing Up

Why has so much space and time been spent on graphs? The answer is simple: they are very important and are becoming more important every day.

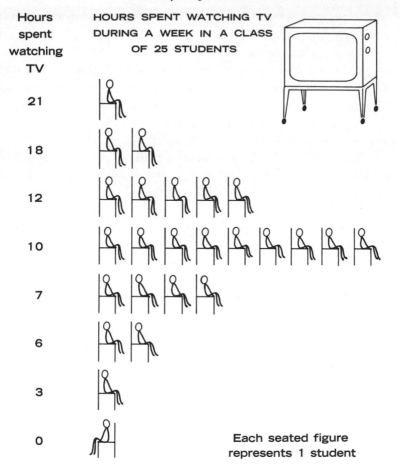

Hours spent watching TV	HOURS SPENT WATCHING TV DURING A WEEK IN A CLASS OF 25 STUDENTS

Each seated figure represents 1 student

Not too many years ago, graphs appeared only in very technical, statistical, or mathematical articles. Almost all the graphs were line graphs. Usually, only other statisticians and mathematicians studied them.

When experts in other fields—business, labor, education, psychology, the physical sciences—began to use statistics to help solve their problems, the graph came into wider use. Many wanted the general public, not only other experts, to be aware of their work. Graphs became more colorful and more attractive. They took on other shapes and forms, such as the bar graph or the pictorial chart. The great advantage of a graph is that it can tell a long story in a short time. And most people can learn to read a graph with only a little effort.

Graphs can also be put to many uses. They are extremely flexible. They spring up in surprising places. Did you know that almost any mathematical equation can be shown on a graph? Did you know that the musical staff system is only a special example of a scientific and mathematical graph?

Today, it is almost impossible to read any business or scientific magazine without finding in it a wide variety of graphs and charts. The important business magazine *Fortune* has scores of them in every issue.

Earlier in this chapter several graphs showing some of the results of important scientific studies were presented. Not too many years ago, the results of this work would have been explained in thousands of words. Only other experts would have read them. Today, although words have not disappeared, simple graphs make it possible for anyone with a little understanding of them to share the experts' knowledge.

2 AVERAGES

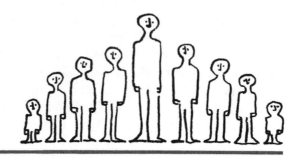

THINK OF THE MANY WAYS in which you have heard the word "average" used. The following examples would probably be on your list:

Talking about the weather

The weather report you hear on radio or on TV usually includes this sentence. "The *average temperature* for this day is 75 degrees."

Talking about people

The *average man* in the United States owns a car.

Talking about baseball

The last ballplayer with a *batting average* over .400 was Ted Williams.

Talking about money

The *average American family* in 1963 had an *average (median) income* of $6,200 per year.

Talking about school

My *math average* is much higher this term than it was last term.

If you think about it, you can probably add to this list. The word "average" is a common one in our language.

Exactly what does it mean?

If you think about the examples given above, you may sense one important fact about an average. *One number* — the average — represents the group. The group may have only 2 members or 200,000,000 members. But that one number (the average) should tell us something about all the other members, or numbers, it represents. How it does this, exactly what it tells us, and even what it does not tell us, we shall soon see. In some situations, the average is known but the individual numbers that it represents are not. Then, the average is the *expected value* of any of the unknown numbers.

In its simplest form, an average is this: the sum of the numbers, or values, divided by the number of numbers, or things. For example, if we want the average of the numbers 1 and 3, we find it as follows:

$$\frac{1+3}{2} = \frac{4 \text{ (the sum of the numbers)}}{2 \text{ (the number of numbers)}} = 2$$

If you are a stamp collector and buy four stamps — one for 10¢, one for 12¢, one for 15¢, and one for 19¢ — what is the average price you paid per stamp?

$$\frac{10+12+15+19}{4} = \frac{56 \text{ (the total value)}}{4 \text{ (the number of things)}} = 14¢ \text{ per stamp}$$

It is as if you had bought 4 stamps at 14 cents each.

Figuring out an average can become much more complicated, but this is the method that is used.

Some History

The idea of an average is a very simple one; yet only in recent times has the use of it become popular and familiar. Of course, mathematicians and scientists have long known that by adding numbers together and dividing by the number of numbers, they would obtain an average. But there didn't seem to be much use for such calculations.

Not until 1830 was the phrase "the average man" first used by a famous Belgian mathematician and social scientist, Adolphe Quetelet. He had taken many kinds of measurements of students and of other groups of people in Belgium. Then, after he had made his calculations, he published information about "the average man." Many people were shocked at this, and some even called Quetelet an ungodly person. But his calculations were useful and soon were widely accepted.

The earliest use of an average seems to have come from certain customs of the sea. When ships were much less safe than they are today, very often part of a ship's cargo was either lost or destroyed at sea. Sometimes, in stormy seas, some cargo had to be thrown overboard to save the ship. The damage to cargo at sea was called by the Latin word *havaria*, from which comes our word "average."

It would have been unjust for the merchant whose cargo was thrown overboard to lose all his money while the rest of the cargo arrived safely. What was done was this: the value of the cargo that arrived safely was divided among all the merchants so that one man would not bear the entire loss. This was a simple form of insurance and the basis of an average.

Let us look at an example that will help us to understand this more clearly.

Suppose 5 merchants each shipped cargo worth $2,500. The value of the ship's total cargo was

$2,500 \times 5 = $12,500$

During a raging storm one man's cargo was washed overboard.

When the ship finally arrived in port, the value of the cargo was

$$\$2,500 \times 4 = \$10,000$$

Ten thousand dollars had to be averaged among 5 men. Therefore, each merchant received

$$\frac{\$10,000}{5} = \$2,000$$

The *average loss* was $500 per merchant rather than $2,500 lost by one.

Averages and Kings

The merchants in sea trade were not the only ones with a personal stake in averages. Centuries ago, kings shared this interest. At that time, most sovereigns had two main concerns. They were:
1. The size of the army they could raise.
2. The amount of taxes they could collect.

If a king could know how much food an average acre would produce and how many acres of farmland were in his kingdom, his minister could calculate the tax receipts. Also, if he knew the ages of his subjects, he could estimate the possible size of his army.

In those days, and almost into the nineteenth century, there were no trained census takers. Most of the king's information about these important questions came from his tax collectors. But they were not very reliable and hardly scientific. Therefore, any really scientific information a king could obtain about these two questions would have been of great value to him.

In 1693, the famous English astronomer, Edmund Halley, after whom Halley's Comet is named, calculated the first life insurance tables. In these tables he showed, *on the average*, how many people of each age would die each year. He showed, also on the average, how many more years a person of any age could expect to live.

Halley's method of calculation was so scientific that modern life insurance tables are still prepared in almost the same way. But Halley's main interest was not in life insurance; it was to show a king how large an army he could expect to raise. In his own words, this is what he wrote when his results were printed:

The first use hereof is to shew [show] the Proportion of Men able to bear Arms in the Multitude [the people], which are those between 18 and 56. . . .

So that the whole Force this City can raise of Fencible Men [soldiers], is about . . . 9/34 or somewhat more than a quarter of the Number of Souls, which may perhaps pass for a Rule for all other places.

It is interesting to know that Halley identified the comet named after him by means of an average. He calculated the average period (length of time) between the appearances of the comet as 76 years. In this way, he predicted when it would appear again. And although he was dead, other astronomers saw it. You may expect it again in 1985.

Averages in Our Lives

You may wonder why there was no progress in the calculation and use of the average until modern times. Certainly there were men in all ages who would have been able to calculate it. Sir Isaac Newton, one of the greatest scientists and mathematicians who ever lived, did much of his work in the seventeenth century. Newton, who developed an entirely new branch of mathematics called the calculus, would almost certainly have been capable of advancing the idea of the average. There was no progress in the statistical average because there was no real use for it.

Think of how men lived in the seventeenth and eighteenth centuries. The average man was a farmer. For the most part, he and his family ate what he grew. His wife baked the family bread. He built his own house according to his needs. Even in the cities, most people did a great many things for themselves. Except for the wealthy, they made their own clothes. The wealthy had them made to order. Shoes were made by cobblers according to a person's measure. There were no large factories producing clothing. Schooling, too, was on a small scale. Almost all of it was private, not public. Few people traveled, and those who did went by horse or by ship. Most people lived simple lives and had simple needs.

Today, life is extremely complicated. Goods are produced in huge factories in tremendous quantities. The bread you eat may come from hundreds of miles away. The house you live in may be one of many exactly like it, all built by someone else. There are thousands of cars on the road exactly like the one you may ride in. The kind of ice cream you eat may be eaten by another boy or girl in every town and city within two hundred miles of you in any direction.

How is it decided how much bread to bake? How much ice cream to make? What flavors? How big a house should be? How many seats a car should have? How many of each size of shirt to make? How many servings a package of frozen food should have?

In today's world, these questions cannot be answered without exact knowledge. Otherwise, companies would lose tremendous amounts of money through failure to sell the things they produce.

Earlier, in giving examples of averages, we wrote, "The *average temperature* for this day is 75 degrees." In centuries gone by, this would have been a useless bit of information, even if it were available. Let us examine the importance of such averages today.

If the average temperature for the day is high, ice-cream sales are bound to be high. The ice cream must be manufactured in advance. After it is made, it must be delivered to where it will be sold. This requires careful planning. It also takes time. The higher the average temperature, the more likely it is that people will go to beaches or parks. Traffic on bridges and highways will be heavier. With more traffic, more gasoline will be sold. All the people involved—park attendants, police, oil-truck drivers, ice-cream salesmen, filling-station attendants—must be prepared for this. You can see that it is of great importance to many people whether the average temperature for August 15 is higher than for July 15.

We shall look at one more simple average and see the part it plays in our lives.

The United States Bureau of the Census, which counts the American people every ten years, reports that the average family size is approximately four persons. This average guides the builders of homes, the packers of food, the makers of cars. Without this bit of knowledge, a good part of American industry could not operate efficiently.

"How is it decided how big a house should be?" we asked. It is decided on the basis of average family size. Today, houses are often built in groups of 50 or 100 or even, in some cases, of 1,000 at a time. If they are not built to house the average American family, they will not be sold. Most American homes built today are most comfortable for a family of four. Of course, bigger homes are constructed, too, but we are talking about the average home. The *average home* is built for the *average family*.

What is true of private homes is true of cars. The average American car is made to be comfortable for four people. Of course, five, six, or even more can squeeze in for short trips. But can you imagine making a 2,000-mile trip with five or six people in the average car? It would not be very comfortable. We know that there are small sports cars for two people, and there are station wagons for larger families. But the size of the average American family determines the size of the average American car.

It is a fact of modern life that every industry must know the averages that are important to it.

The Family of Averages

When a person uses the word "average," he usually has in mind the *mean*. This is the most common type of average. We will soon see what it is and how it is calculated. But the family of averages has many members. The things we want to know or the kinds of numbers we are dealing with may require different kinds of averages. The purpose for which the average will be used may also help decide which one will be most useful.

An average is a *measure of central tendency*. This simply states that an average is a point around which the numbers group. *All* the numbers, not *many*, determine the average.

An average should act as a representative of the group of numbers. It should tell us something about the numbers from which it comes. If it doesn't, it is useless. An average of a few numbers scattered in every direction usually serves no purpose.

The following story will help to make this clear.

Two men meet and start a discussion about homes. One man asks, "How old are the homes on Elm Street?"

The other man thinks a while, then answers, "The average home is about 35 years old."

It turns out that there are 3 homes on the street. One house was just completed; another is 2 years old; the third is a Civil War relic, 103 years old.

It is true that the average home is 35 years old:

$$\frac{0 + 2 + 103}{3} = \frac{105 \ (\textit{the sum of the ages})}{3 \ \ (\textit{the number of homes})}$$
$$= 35 \text{ years } (\textit{average age})$$

But what does this average tell us? Absolutely nothing! It is not representative; it is not typical of the group. Actually, it misleads us. If the man had said, "Two homes are practically new. The third was built during the Civil War," he would have given us more correct information.

You should always keep this in mind in dealing with averages.

The mean

Mean means *center*. To picture this, imagine a whole group of numbers going around and around in a kind of folk dance. After a while the dancers move toward the center of the circle and choose partners. One dancer remains in the center, standing alone. This dancer—the average—is the representative of the entire group.

As the dancers chose partners, 25 joined 75; 2 joined 98; 40 joined 60; and so on.

Of course, an average can be easily calculated even when numbers do not form pairs as they do in this illustration.

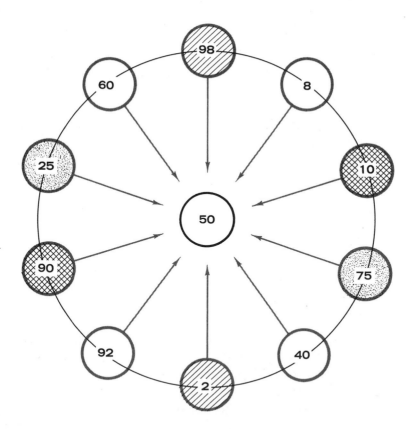

By calculating the average, we can see that 50 was the "center" toward which our collection of numbers was moving:

Numbers
2
8
10
25
40
50
60
75
90
92
98
―――
550

$$\frac{550 \;(\textit{the sum of the numbers})}{11 \;\;(\textit{the number of numbers})} = 50 \;(\textit{average})$$

With only a few numbers, calculating the average is simple. But even when many numbers are involved, the method is only a little more complicated.

If we had to find the average of 1,000 numbers, it would take us quite some time to list them all. Also, in adding them, we would be very likely to make mistakes. We would also need a lot of paper. For these reasons—to save time, to save work, to avoid mistakes—we use shortcuts to find the average of many numbers.

We begin by making an arrangement with three columns:

Column 1	*Column 2*	*Column 3*
The thing we want to average	*The number of times it occurs*	*Column 1 × Column 2*

Column 1. In this column, we list, in order, the thing we are averaging. It may be class marks, wages, the height of people, the number of children in families, etc.

Column 2. In this column, we enter the number of times we found each mark, or wage, or height, etc.

Column 3. On every line, multiply (×) the number in column 1 by the number in column 2.

When all the multiplications have been made, add the numbers in column 2 to get the total; do the same in column 3.

To find the average, *divide the total in column 3 by the total in column 2.*

Glee and gloom

Jane and Alice, two close friends, are in different classes in the same school. One day they meet in the lunchroom.

Jane is excited and happy. "Oh, Alice, I got an 80 on my math test."

Very sadly, Alice replies, "I got an 80, too."

With the same mark, why was Jane happy while Alice was unhappy?

The class average may be a clue.

JANE'S CLASS

Column 1 Mark on test	Column 2 Number of students receiving mark	Column 3 Column 1 × Column 2
85	1	85
80	1	80
75	3	225
70	7	490
65	5	325
60	3	180
50	4	200
40	1	40
Total	25	1,625

$$\frac{1,625 \quad (sum\ of\ all\ marks)}{25 \quad (number\ of\ students)}$$

$$= 65\ (average\ mark)$$

ALICE'S CLASS

Column 1 Mark on test	Column 2 Number of students receiving mark	Column 3 Column 1 × Column 2
100	5	500
90	6	540
80	8	640
75	5	375
70	1	70
Total	25	2,125

$$\frac{2,125 \quad (sum\ of\ all\ marks)}{25 \quad (number\ of\ students)}$$

$$= 85\ (average\ mark)$$

The averages throw some light on Jane's glee and Alice's gloom. Jane's mark was well above the average of her class; Alice's was lower than the average.

The average gives us a clue to every member of the group it represents. A mark standing by itself does not tell us the whole story.

This method of finding an average can be used for few or many numbers. In some cases, still further shortcuts are used. For example, the numbers in column 1 may be grouped to include several numbers. When government statisticians average family income in the United States, they form a frequency distribution such as this:

Yearly family income	Number of families
Less than $1,000	500,000
$1,000 but less than $2,000	1,000,000
$2,000 but less than $3,000	2,500,000

Since family income may extend from 0 (nothing) to more than $1,000,000 per year, they could not use column 1 exactly as we did. But the final table does not look much different from the first two columns of our table.

Finding the hidden numbers

With the mean, we have some idea of the kind of numbers it represents, but the whole story is still a mystery. You may know that a test average is 65. It is possible, although not probable, that everyone taking the test received exactly 65.

To clear up the mystery of the hidden numbers that made up an average, another measure is necessary. It is called the *standard deviation*. The two measures go together like star and satellite. (Deviation here means simply the distance from the mean.) If we know the *mean* and the *standard deviation* of a group of numbers, no matter how large, this is what we know about them:

The mean + 1 standard deviation and − 1 standard deviation	Will include about 2 out of 3 numbers in the group.
The mean + 2 standard deviations and − 2 standard deviations	Will include about 95 out of 100 numbers in the group.
The mean + 3 standard deviations and − 3 standard deviations	Will include 997 numbers out of 1,000, if there are enough numbers, or 99.7 percent of the numbers in the group.

Let us see what this measure tells us about the marks in Jane's class. The average mark (mean) we figured out as 65. The standard deviation is approximately 10. (We will not calculate the standard deviation here. The process is somewhat complicated. Those interested will find the calculation for Jane's class in the Answer Section.)

1. The mean (65) + 1 standard deviation (10) = 75
   The mean (65) − 1 standard deviation (10) = 55

   Therefore, 2 out of 3 marks, approximately 17 marks in a class of 25, should be between 55 and 75.
   Actually, there are 18 such marks — very close to what we would expect.

2. The mean (65) + 2 standard deviations (20) = 85
   The mean (65) − 2 standard deviations (20) = 45

   Therefore, 95 percent of the marks should be between 45 and 85.
   Actually 24 out of the 25 marks, or 96 percent, fall between 45 and 85. Again, very close.

As one might expect, the larger the group of numbers from which our mean and standard deviation are calculated, the more accurate will be the information they give us.

There can be no doubt that the mystery of the hidden numbers is cleared up by the standard deviation.

Here's a puzzler. If everyone in a class received 65 on a test, the mean would be 65. What would be the standard deviation? (See the Answer Section.)

Special baseball section

Before we move on to other averages, we will discuss an "average" that is not really an average. This is the familiar batting average of baseball players. A batting average is really a batting percentage. To find a batting average we have to know:

1. The number of hits he made.
2. The number of times he was officially at bat.

This is how a .300 batting average may be calculated:

$$\frac{150 \quad (the\ number\ of\ hits)}{500\ (the\ number\ of\ times\ at\ bat)}$$

$$\frac{.300\ batting\ average}{500\sqrt{150.000}}$$

On the basis of a .300 batting percentage, we can say, "On the average, he will make 3 hits for every 10 times at bat."

If you like puzzles, here is one. We will now calculate the average in another way. The batting average is a special kind of average (mean) of every day's average.

Let us take 10 playing days in the season of our imaginary .300 hitter. Here is what he did:

Column 1	Column 2	Column 3	Column 4
		Average:	*Column 2*
Number of	*Number of*	*column 1*	×
hits	*times at bat*	*column 2*	*column 3*
3	6	.500	3.000
2	5	.400	2.000
0	3	.000	.000
1	3	.333	.999
2	3	.667	2.001
2	2	1.000	2.000
1	5	.200	1.000
0	3	.000	.000
1	5	.200	1.000
0	5	.000	.000
12	40		12.000

We can calculate his average in two ways:

1. $\dfrac{\text{Column 1} \quad (\textit{the total number of hits})}{\text{Column 2} \; (\textit{the total number of times at bat})} = \dfrac{12}{40} = .300$

2. $\dfrac{\text{Column 4}}{\text{Column 2}} = \dfrac{12.000}{40} = .300$

(We do not need to know the number of hits he made if we know his daily average and his times at bat.)

We have now calculated a *weighted average.* See the Answer Section for the calculation of a weighted average in connection with an important governmental statistic.

As any baseball fan knows, a "heavy hitter" is more valuable to a team, usually, than a player who hits only singles. To measure the power of a "heavy hitter," at the end of a season a special average is calculated. This is called the *slugging average.*

We will calculate the slugging average of our .300 hitter who made 150 hits in 500 times at bat. The 150 hits included:

singles	105
doubles	15
triples	5
home runs	25

We now multiply the number of hits by the number of bases per hit:

	Column 1 Number of hits	Column 2 Number of bases per hit	Column 1 × column 2
Singles	105	1	105
Doubles	15	2	30
Triples	5	3	15
Home runs	25	4	100
			250

The total of 250 is called "total base hits." Dividing this by the number of times at bat gives us the slugging average. The slugging average is also a *weighted average*. The "weight" is the number of bases represented by singles, doubles, triples, or home runs.

$$\frac{250\ (total\ base\ hits)}{500\ (number\ of\ times\ at\ bat)} = .500$$

So, our .300 hitter has a *slugging average* of .500, which makes him a very valuable man, indeed.

The mode

Your mother might say in conversation, "This spring the mode is brown." She would mean that the color brown is the fashion in women's clothing. Most women will be wearing brown.

In statistics, the *mode* is an average. It is an average you can see by merely looking at the numbers. It is the one number that occurs much more often than any other number in the group.

Let us analyze one example.

In a certain school, the students are asked to bring in contributions to the Red Cross. All who wish to do so bring in their money on a set day. A week later, the poster on the next page appears on the bulletin board.

Just by looking at the numbers, you can see that the *mode* is 25 cents. This amount was contributed by 400 pupils, more by far than contributed any other amount.

Is it representative of the group? It is. Is it a typical number? It is. Does it tell us something about the group? It does. Even if we were told only that 400 of the 1,000 pupils contributed 25 cents each, we would have a good deal of information. We could also guess that some contributed less—but probably not too much less—and that some contributed more—but probably not too much more.

The mode should stand out. Since we found the mode with-

RED CROSS DRIVE A GREAT SUCCESS

The following contributions were made to the Red Cross by the pupils of this school.

Amount of contribution	Number of students contributing
0	25
5 cents	40
10 cents	100
15 cents	80
20 cents	100
25 cents	400
30 cents	80
35 cents	70
40 cents	50
50 cents	30
75 cents	10
$1.00	15
	1,000
Total amount contributed	$250.00

---

out any calculation, we cannot say by how much it should stand out. Even among statisticians, common sense is usually the guide.

In the following case there is no mode:

Group	Number in group
A	98
B	105
C	102
D	107

Although Group D has more in its group than any other, it really does not stand out.

The mode is used as a rough average. When we don't have time for calculations, we might use it. We would also use it when there is no real need for a more exact average.

The median

The median is used much more often than the mode. It is a very handy type of average in studying the wages people earn.

Median means *middle*. This is why it is called an *average of position*. In a group of numbers arranged in order, it is the one number that divides everything in half. When we know the median of a group of numbers, we know that there are just as many numbers above it as there are below it.

The story of the two men discussing the ages of the homes on Elm Street showed that an average — the mean — can mislead us. In that case, even a median would not have helped. There are situations, however, where a mean would mislead us but a median would give us useful information.

In one high school, symphony orchestra tickets were sold at reduced rates to encourage attendance. At the end of the season, several students were asked how many concerts they had attended. Here are their answers:

1 student	0 (no concerts)
1 student	0 (no concerts)
1 student	1 concert
1 student	2 concerts
1 student	3 concerts
1 student	4 concerts

The answers, so far, are not unusual. The next student we stop, however, happens to be the son of the orchestra's conductor. He can get in free. He attends every concert he can. His answer is "25 concerts."

We now have 7 students who attended a total of 35 concerts. There certainly is no *mode* and the simple *mean* is:

$$\frac{35 \ (\textit{total number of concerts})}{7 \ (\textit{total number of students})} = 5 \text{ concerts per student}$$

This would be a misleading average. Not one student, except the conductor's son, attended 5 concerts. And he attended many more. This average gives us no information.

By arranging the number of concerts attended in order, we can easily find the median:

Number of concerts		Number of students	
0		1	
0		1	
1		1	
2	←	1	← median
3		1	
4		1	
25		1	

The middle student attended 2 concerts, and that is our median. Now we can say that just as many students attended less than 2 concerts as attended more. This is a more accurate description of the information we had.

The median is useful when one person or a few persons or events are so different from all the others that they completely change the *mean* when they are included. This is why the *median* is often used for averaging wages or income. If a few persons earn an unusually high amount while everyone else earns close to a much smaller amount, other averages may mislead us.

Shopping for averages at a supermarket

At a medium-sized supermarket, where your mother might do her shopping, there are 41 employees. Let us find out the average weekly wage.

As in most supermarkets, there are stock clerks, check-out people and their helpers, a section manager or two. There are some people who work only part time. There are also a store manager and his assistant manager. These are the weekly earnings in the store:

Weekly earnings	Number of workers receiving them	Adding employees as we move down
$ 20	3	3
25	4	7
35	8	15
40	3	18
45	3	21
50	10	
60	6	
75	2	
250	1 (asst. manager)	
300	1 (manager)	
	41	

If you compute the mean (average) of all the employees by the method discussed earlier, you will find that it is $55.00 per week. A glance at the table shows that the few high wages had a very strong influence on the average. Only 10 of the 41 employees earned more than the average of $55.00. If you calculate the average (mean) without the manager and assistant manager, you will find that it is now about $43.70. The wages of these two men alone raised the average wage about $11.30.

Since we want an average of all employees, we cannot eliminate the two men. In such a case, our best description of all wages will be a *median*. The median earner will be the twenty-first employee. (There will be 20 earning as much or less, and 20 earning as much or more.)

As we count the employees from lowest to highest, we find that the twenty-first person earns $45.00 per week. So we can say: 50 percent (half) of the employees earn $45 per week or less; 50 percent earn $45 or more. We have described the earnings without the heavy influence of the managers.

With very slight changes for large sets of numbers and for numbers arranged in groups, this way of finding a median is used in almost all cases.

We have discussed the most important members of the family of averages. They should look less strange to you in the future.

3 PROBABILITY

WE SET OUT now on an exciting adventure. Our aim is to explore the world of *probability*. It is not an unknown world. Great men have explored it before us and have marked our road well, but it still remains a world of great fascination and challenge. For those who love a challenge, there will be great rewards.

The earliest known explorers of the world of probability were gamblers. These men were interested only in winning money at games of chance. In this, they were not too different from some of the great explorers of the globe. But the gamblers were soon followed by mathematicians and scientists.

At first, the mathematicians looked upon probability as an interesting exercise. They soon recognized it, however, as a powerful mathematical tool for solving problems that had previously puzzled them.

Although probability was born in the scheming mind of the gambler, its real parents were mathematicians, scientists, and philosophers. Today, gamblers still live by the laws of probability. Their use of it, though, is insignificant. Its importance

53

lies in the part it plays in practically all human affairs. As the great French mathematician and scientist, Pierre Simon Laplace, wrote in the early nineteenth century, "It is remarkable that a science which began with the consideration of games of chance should have become the most important object of human knowledge."

The word "probability" is a simple one. "What is probable?" means "What is likely?" Probability is, therefore, the likelihood of an event. We can also say that probability is chance. Sometimes, instead of saying, "What are the chances?" we say, "What are the odds?"

Chance is also accident, or luck. Very often we say that something happened "by chance." We may mean that the event happened by luck, good or bad, or that it happened by accident.

Probability is, therefore, likelihood or chance or odds or luck or accident. If you stop to think about it, you will soon realize that all these expressions have one thing in common — *uncertainty*. The laws of probability are the laws of chance or the laws of uncertainty.

Probability often deals with events before they happen. The coin is in the air — will it fall heads or tails? The car is on the road — will it be involved in an accident? The atomic particles are moving in a chamber — will they collide? How long will the light bulb last? When will the razor blade become dull? Do such questions have answers? They do — as we shall see.

You may now begin to wonder: If probability is chance or luck or uncertainty, how can there be laws about it? Many men have asked this question in the past. Before you complete this chapter, you will learn that there are many laws. You will also discover that the laws are, in fact, very strict.

Nothing seems to be as "accidental" as an automobile accident, but every holiday weekend the National Safety Council predicts how many people will be killed in such accidents. And, unfortunately, its prediction is usually quite accurate.

The laws of probability give us the power to predict events

about which we can have no exact knowledge. We can say *how likely* it is that an event will happen; exactly *how much chance* there is; exactly *how great* are the odds for or against it. In addition, the laws of probability tell us how sure we can be of our prediction, how much *confidence* we can have in it.

As early as the seventeenth century, mathematicians began the serious study of probability. Many important discoveries in the field date from that time. Since then, interest in the subject has increased rather than lessened. Today, it is an important branch of mathematics. The men who specialize in it are called "probabilists."

Two of the outstanding probabilists of our day are Professor William Feller of Princeton University and Professor Frederick Mosteller of Harvard University. These men have written important books on the subject of probability. Some day you may read them. If you do, one thing will surely strike you. Probabilists enjoy their work! Professor Mosteller writes of the "beauty" of probability; Professor Feller talks of its "charm." And Dr. Warren Weaver, a famous scientist, writes about it as "fun."

You, too, will find all these things. All you need is the proper spirit of adventure.

Experienced explorers always equip themselves with good tools. Mountain climbers carry well-made picks and sturdy ropes. Deep-sea divers seek the best breathing equipment. For our voyage into the world of probability, we will also require some tools. Without them, our trip would be foolhardy, perhaps even painful. With them, our voyage will be full of pleasant moments of discovery.

The tools we need are those of the mind. Therefore, we enrich ourselves as we acquire them. This is what we need.

1. *Equations:* What they are and how to handle them.

2. *The powers of numbers:* Squares, cubes, and higher powers.

3. *The roots of numbers:* Powers in reverse.

4. *Factorial numbers:* Numbers in special series.

5. *New words in our vocabulary:* These we will acquire as we go along.

It is possible that you already "own" some of these tools. So much the better. You may sharpen them up or move along.

Equations

An equation is like a seesaw in balance. When equal amounts are added to or subtracted from the two expressions on either side of the equal sign, the balance is maintained. A more precise way of stating it is that the two expressions represent the same number.

Take this simple equation:

$$a + b = c$$

You know that $a + b$ and c represent the same number. As a matter of fact, the "equal" sign can be read as "is the same number as." If we were to read the above equation as a statement, we could say "$a + b$ is the same number as c."

In order to keep an equation in balance, *the same number* may always be added to or subtracted from *both* of the original expressions. Then the new expressions still form an equation because they represent the same (new) number.

Suppose, in the equation $a + b = c$, that

$$a = 2 \quad \text{and} \quad c = 5$$

What is the value of b?

$$2 + b = 5$$

Obviously, b must be 3.

Suppose the missing number were not so obvious, as in the equation $265 + b = 713$. If b were to stand alone as one expression of the missing number, the other expression should give a number equal to b. This can be accomplished by adding some number to or subtracting some number from both sides of the equation. Thus

$$265 + b = 713$$
$$265 + b - 265 = 713 - 265$$
$$b = 448, \text{ the missing number}$$

This is exactly what could have been done in the first example had it not been so obvious. Knowing that

$$2 + b = 5$$

we could have subtracted 2 from each expression, giving

$$2 + b - 2 = 5 - 2$$
$$b = 3$$

Sometimes one must add a number to each expression, as in the equation, $11 = k - 4$, where we want to find k. Then, to have k stand alone, we would add 4 to each expression.

$$11 + 4 = k - 4 + 4$$
$$k = 15$$

We have solved some simple equations. Complicated ones have only more parts. They are just as easy to solve if you follow the rules.

Let us apply what we have learned to find the value of b in the following equation:

$$10a + 5b = 7c$$

Again, let

$$a = 2 \quad \text{and} \quad c = 5$$

(*Reminder:* Numbers and letters written together are multiplied. For example, $10a$ means $10 \times a$; abc means $a \times b \times c$.) By substituting numbers for letters, we have

$$10 \times 2 + 5b = 7 \times 5$$

or

$$20 + 5b = 35$$

Again, the same number may be subtracted from both

expressions, and our new equation is

$$20 + 5b - 20 = 35 - 20$$

or

$$5b = 15$$

Since $5b$ is the same as $5 \times b$, the value of b is obviously 3.

But suppose, again, that the numbers were much larger. In that case, we can maintain the "balance" of the equation in another way.

An equation will remain "in balance" if both expressions of the equation are multiplied or divided by the same number. In this way, $5b = 15$ may be simplified to

$$\frac{5b}{5} = \frac{5}{5} \times b = \frac{15}{5}$$
$$b = 3$$

As a final step, we will now put to use everything we have learned to solve the following equation:

$$10a + 5ab + 3abc - 4bc + 10b = 110$$

Again, let

$$a = 2, \qquad c = 5, \qquad b = ?$$

After substituting numbers for letters, our equation becomes

$$(10 \times 2) + (5 \times 2 \times b) + (3 \times 2 \times b \times 5) - (4 \times b \times 5)$$
$$+ (10b) = 110$$

We may have a lot of numbers, but they are all pretty simple ones. Let's complete the multiplications.

The result now is

$$20 + 10b + 30b - 20b + 10b = 110$$

After adding up the b values, we have

$$30b + 20 = 110$$

Then

$$30b + 20 - 20 = 110 - 20$$
$$30b = 90$$

Then

$$\frac{30b}{30} = \frac{30}{30} \times b = \frac{90}{30}$$
$$b = 3$$

This is the fun in solving equations. From what seem like very complicated arrangements, we end up with a very simple and tidy result.

You should now be able to tackle almost any similar equation with confidence.

The Power of a Number

There are times when it is necessary to multiply a number by itself one or more times. Mathematicians use a signal, or shortcut, to show that this has to be done. For example, we want to multiply 3×3. It is shown this way:

3^2

This is the same as saying, "Multiply the number 3 by itself." Or, in other words, "Use the number 3 twice in a multiplication," or "Use the number 3 twice as a factor."

If we want to multiply $3 \times 3 \times 3 = 27$, we show it as:

$3^3 = 27$

You can see how handy this method is. Writing 3^2 instead of 3×3 may not be much of a saving. But suppose that you had to write out a number like 10^{75}. Numbers of this size are very common, especially in physics and astronomy.

In this system of writing, there are special names for the two members of the set. You should become familiar with them.

this is the *base* → 3^2 ← this is the *exponent*

The *base* is the number we are going to multiply. The *exponent* is the *power* of the number—the number of times the base will be used as a factor.

The exponent is always written in the upper right-hand corner of the base. It is usually written in a smaller size.

A few common expressions are used in connection with such numbers.

3^2 is called: 3 squared
3^3 is called: 3 cubed

For higher exponents, we simply say, "3 to the fourth power" for 3^4; or "3 to the fifth power" for 3^5, and so on.

As a reminder,

$2^3 = 2 \times 2 \times 2 = 8$
$10^5 = 10 \times 10 \times 10 \times 10 \times 10 = 100,000$

Unknown numbers: letters

We use the same signals (or symbols) when we work with letters instead of numbers. Until we find the value of a, we write a^2. This tells us that when we do find the value of a, we must square it—or multiply it by itself.

When combinations of letters are used to stand for unknown numbers, we must be sure to read the signals correctly. Suppose we have ab^2. This is the same as $a \times b^2$. Therefore, in this combination only b is squared.

If we wanted the product of $a \times b$ (or ab) squared, we would have to write it $(ab)^2$.

This tells us that when you find the value of a and the value of b, multiply one by the other and square the product.

To see how important this is, we will go back to numbers. Suppose we have 5×2^2. This is the same as $5 \times 4 = 20$. If we wanted the product of 5×2, squared, we would have to write it $(5 \times 2)^2$. This is the same as $(10)^2 = 100$.

When numbers and letters are combined, we follow the

same rules. Suppose we have $2a^2$. If we find out that $a = 5$, we can then write $2(5^2) = 2(25) = 50$.

As you continue with your studies, you will discover that mathematicians, including statisticians, and scientists dislike unnecessary work. Therefore, they have developed many short-cuts to write out their problems or results. Since the squaring of numbers is so often necessary, there are standard tables of squares. You can find such tables in almost all statistics books. Some books even have tables of cubed numbers (the third power of a number). But these are not so common because they take up a lot of room. The results of cubed numbers grow very rapidly. For example, the cube of 1,000 (or $1,000^3$) = 1,000,000,000.

Summary

You should learn to square and cube numbers or to raise them to any power (or exponent). Tables of squares are useful when there are many numbers to be squared. No statistician would use them for two or three numbers. It would take longer to find the book and look them up than to calculate them.

Using everything that you have learned about equations and exponents, can you find the value of b in the following equation?

$$a^3 + 2a^2b + ab + 10c + 2c^2 - 20 = 118$$
$$a = 2 \qquad\qquad\qquad c = 5$$
$$b = ?$$

If you have any difficulty with this problem, you can find the solution in the Answer Section.

At the Sign of the Square Root

Much has been said about the mathematician's use of signs and symbols. He uses them to indicate that a number, or letter, stands for something other than what it is or that you must treat it in a special way.

One of the most attractive symbols is the *square-root sign.* It is shown as $\sqrt{}$. In some books it is called the *radical* sign. Under this sign, you will always find a number, a letter, or a combination of the two.

The sign says this: Find a number that you can multiply by itself to equal the number under the sign. In other words, what is the *square root* of the number you see?

If you see this, $\sqrt{4}$, you must ask yourself: What number, multiplied by itself, will equal 4? The answer is, of course, 2. Technically, we would then say, "The square root of 4 is 2." It should now be clear that taking a square root is the opposite of squaring a number.

From what you already know about mathematicians and statisticians, you might guess that long tables of the square roots of numbers already exist. You would be right. Almost no statistics book is complete without them. But you should know how to find a square root without a book. Books are not always available. And who would search for a book to find two square roots?

Calculating square roots

When the square root of a number contains only one digit, without any remainder, the calculation is made mentally. For example:

$$\sqrt{1} = 1 \quad (1 \times 1 = 1)$$
$$\sqrt{4} = 2 \quad (2 \times 2 = 4)$$
$$\sqrt{25} = 5 \quad (5 \times 5 = 25)$$
$$\sqrt{81} = 9 \quad (9 \times 9 = 81)$$

Your ability to do mental multiplication will set the limit to the numbers whose square roots you can find without calculation.

The names given to the different parts of a division problem will be used to explain how to find a square root. To refresh your memory, these are the parts:

$$\begin{array}{r} 5 \leftarrow \text{QUOTIENT} \\ \text{DIVISOR} \rightarrow 25\overline{)130} \leftarrow \text{DIVIDEND} \\ \underline{125} \\ 5 \leftarrow \text{REMAINDER} \end{array}$$

PROBLEM 1: $\sqrt{2,025} = ?$

Step 1. Starting from the *right* (the "units" or "ones" position), divide the number (the DIVIDEND) into *pairs* of digits.

$$\sqrt{20'25}$$

There will be as many digits in your *answer* as there are *pairs* of numbers. Here, two pairs of numbers indicate a two-digit answer.

Step 2. Starting with the first pair on the left (20) ask yourself: What is the *largest* number, multiplied by itself, that can go into 20? The answer is 4. (3 would not be the largest number; 5 would be too high, since $5 \times 5 = 25$.)

Place this number (4) in the QUOTIENT and in the DIVISOR. Multiply them. Subtract the product from the first pair. This is how your worksheet should now look:

$$\begin{array}{r} 4 \\ 4\sqrt{20'25} \\ \underline{-16} \\ 4 \leftarrow \text{REMAINDER} \end{array}$$

(Note: The REMAINDER may be *equal to or greater than* the DIVISOR. Don't let this worry you if you have found the largest number. This is not division.)

Step 3. From the DIVIDEND bring down the next pair of digits (25) to join the REMAINDER.

$$\begin{array}{r} 4 \\ \sqrt{20'25} \\ \underline{-16} \\ 4\ 25 \end{array}$$

Step 4. *Double* the QUOTIENT and bring it down as a new DIVISOR. *Leave a space to its right for another digit.*

$$\begin{array}{r} 4 \\ 4\sqrt{20'25} \\ -16 \\ \hline 8\_ \mid \ \ 4\ 25 \end{array}$$

The "8_" now really stands for "80 something." It will change to the 80's as soon as you fill the space.

Step 5. Ask yourself: What number can I now place in the QUOTIENT and in the new "units" (or "ones") position of the DIVISOR so that I will be closest to 425 (but not over), the new DIVIDEND, when I multiply?

Then, multiply *only the new number* in the QUOTIENT by the new DIVISOR.

$$\begin{array}{r} 4\ \ 5 \\ 4\sqrt{20'25} \\ -16 \\ \hline 8\ \underline{5}\ \mid \ \ 4\ 25 \\ -4\ 25 \\ \hline 0\ 00 \end{array}$$

(*Note:* In this step, you may want to try out different numbers until you come closest to 425. Your work sheet may look like this:

$$\begin{array}{cc} 84 & 85 \\ \times\ 4 & \times\ 5 \\ \hline 336 & 425 \end{array}$$

This is one way of testing to see which comes closest to the number you want.)

The process is completed after you have brought down every pair and your REMAINDER is zero (0).

Therefore, the square root of 2,025 is 45. You can check this by multiplying 45 by itself.

We will try one more problem, with some new twists to it, using the five steps.

PROBLEM 2: $\sqrt{93,025} = ?$.

Step 1. Making pairs:

$$\sqrt{9'30'25}$$

(*Note:* When there is an odd number of digits in the number, the first "pair" will have only one digit. It's as if the first pair above were 09.)
Step 2. Finding the highest number for the first pair:

$$\begin{array}{r} 3\phantom{\sqrt{9'30'25}} \\ 3\sqrt{9'30'25} \\ -9 \\ \hline 0 \end{array}$$

(*Note:* The REMAINDER is zero (0), but we have more pairs to bring down.)
Step 3. Bringing down the next pair:

$$\begin{array}{r} 3\phantom{\sqrt{9'30'25}} \\ 3\sqrt{9'30'25} \\ -9 \\ \hline 0\ 30 \end{array}$$

Step 4. Doubling the QUOTIENT—leaving space to the right of new DIVISOR:

$$\begin{array}{r} 3\phantom{\sqrt{9'30'25}} \\ 3\sqrt{9'30'25} \\ -9 \\ \hline 6\ \underline{}\quad 0\ 30 \end{array}$$

(*Note:* It is now obvious that we cannot multiply 60's (6 _) by any number and come under or up to 30. The smallest result we could get would be $1 \times 61 = 61$. In such cases, we place a zero (0) in the QUOTIENT and DIVISOR and continue. It's as if we did this: $0 \times 60 = 000$.)

$$\begin{array}{r} 3\ \ 0\phantom{\sqrt{9'30'25}} \\ 3\sqrt{9'30'25} \\ -9 \\ 6\ \underline{0}\ \overline{|\ 0\ 30} \\ 0\ 00 \\ \hline 30 \end{array}$$

Back to step 3. Bringing down the next pair:

$$
\begin{array}{r}
3 \quad 0 \\
3\sqrt{9'30'25} \\
-9 \\
\end{array}
$$

$$
\begin{array}{r}
60 \overline{0\ 30} \\
-0\ 00 \\
\hline
30\ 25
\end{array}
$$

Step 4. Doubling the QUOTIENT—leaving space to the right of new DIVISOR:

$$
\begin{array}{r}
3 \quad 0 \\
3\sqrt{9'30'25} \\
-9 \\
\end{array}
$$

$$
\begin{array}{r}
60 \overline{0\ 30} \\
-0\ 00 \\
\hline
60\_ \qquad 30\ 25
\end{array}
$$

Step 5. Finding a number for the "units" position of the QUOTIENT and DIVISOR:

$$
\begin{array}{r}
3 \quad 0 \quad 5 \\
3\sqrt{9'30'25} \\
-9 \\
\end{array}
$$

$$
\begin{array}{r}
60 \overline{0\ 30} \\
-0\ 00 \\
\end{array}
$$

$$
\begin{array}{r}
605 \overline{\quad 30\ 25} \\
-30\ 25 \\
\hline
00\ 00
\end{array}
$$

Since there are no more pairs to bring down and the REMAINDER is zero (0), the square root of 93,025 = 305.

As you can see, steps 3, 4, and 5 are repeated as often as there are pairs of numbers to bring down.

Try to find the square roots of larger and larger numbers by following the steps carefully. The best way to start is to multiply any number by itself. Then, "unsquare" it by finding the square root. (To learn how to find the square roots of numbers that do not "come out even" or the roots of decimal numbers, see the Answer Section.)

Factorial Numbers

In many states, before you are allowed to drive a car, you must prove that you can identify certain common symbols, or signals. The symbols may be those for a winding road, a narrow bridge, or a railroad crossing. The same symbols are used everywhere in the United States. Most foreign countries also use them.

This fact should not surprise you. Suppose that a man is driving in a country whose language he doesn't understand. An explanation would be of no help to him, but a familiar symbol, or signal, would warn him of what lies ahead.

An agreed-upon symbol is usually better than a lot of words. A man driving at night might miss the warning, "Winding Road," but he would probably recognize the familiar zigzag lines. Suppose that he were coming to a narrow bridge that ended before a railroad crossing, after which a steep road began. He would most likely pass a warning sign before he could read all that, but symbols would warn him at a glance.

Mathematicians use symbols in the same way. And these, too, are the same all over the world.

A symbol after a number says, "Be alert! Something special has to be done with this number."

One of the most familiar symbols, especially in probability, is an exclamation mark (!) after a number. It is written in this way:

5!

This is read as 5 factorial. It is called a *factorial number*. It tells us: Starting with the number 5, multiply every whole number down the scale to 1. In other words, do this:

$$5 \times 4 \times 3 \times 2 \times 1 = 120$$

To write it this way requires a lot of writing. Imagine if you had to multiply every number from 50 down to 1. In probability, it is often necessary to multiply numbers in a series down to 1. Instead of writing long instructions, or a long chain of numbers, a mathematician uses a symbol.

Remember:

$$1! \text{ means } \qquad 1$$
$$2! \text{ means } \quad 2 \times 1 = 2$$
$$3! \text{ means } 3 \times 2 \times 1 = 6$$

The values of factorial numbers increase very rapidly. The table below shows the values of only the first few factorial numbers.

Factorial number	*Equal to in numbers*
1!	1
2!	2
3!	6
4!	24
5!	120
6!	720
7!	5,040
8!	40,320
9!	362,880
10!	3,628,800
11!	39,916,800
12!	479,001,600
13!	6,227,020,800
14!	87,178,291,200
15!	1,307,674,368,000

You will also meet a strange-looking number called "zero factorial." It is written, as you might expect, 0!. It always has a value of 1.

There is no way to multiply factorial numbers directly. You must first find their separate values. For example, if you need the product of $3! \times 5!$, you must find the values of the factorial numbers and then multiply. Thus

$$3! \times 5! = 6 \times 120 = 720$$

Dividing factorial numbers

Some division of factorial numbers is possible. Remember that if you have a certain number in the numerator of a fraction and the same number in the denominator, you can simplify the fraction by separating out any pair whose quotient is 1. For example, when you had

$$\frac{2 \times 3}{2 \times 5}$$

you could write it as $\frac{2}{2} \times \frac{3}{5} = 1 \times \frac{3}{5} = \frac{3}{5}$

In the same way, $\frac{2a}{3a}$ becomes $\frac{2}{3} \times \frac{a}{a} = \frac{2}{3} \times 1 = \frac{2}{3}$

Exactly the same thing can be done with factorial numbers. Suppose you have

$$\frac{10!}{9!}$$

If you stop to think about it, you will quickly recognize that 10! is the same as 10 × 9!. If written out in full, the 9's, 8's, 7's, 6's, 5's, 4's, 3's, 2's, and 1's appearing in both numerator and denominator form pairs each equal to $\frac{1}{1}$ or 1, leaving only 10 in the numerator. Therefore, you can write the above fraction this way:

$$\frac{10 \times 9!}{9!}, \quad \text{which becomes: } 10 \times \frac{9!}{9!} = 10 \times 1 = 10$$

Another example of the simplifying method can be seen in

$$\frac{50!}{48!}$$

We can write this as

$$\frac{50 \times 49 \times 48!}{48!} = 50 \times 49 = 2{,}450$$

Even more complicated factorial simplification is possible. Take the following, for example:

$$\frac{10!}{10 \times 6!} \quad \text{This becomes:} \quad \frac{10 \times 9 \times 8 \times 7 \times 6!}{10 \times 6!}$$

$$= \frac{10}{10} \times \frac{6!}{6!} \times \frac{9 \times 8 \times 7}{1}$$

Since $\frac{10}{10} = 1$ and $\frac{6!}{6!} = 1$, there is left only

$$\frac{9 \times 8 \times 7}{1} = 504$$

(*Note:* For those who are familiar with the older method of cancellation of equal values in both numerator and denominator, this, too, will simplify factorial fractions.)

When you become familiar with factorial numbers, you will be able to skip steps.

Factorial numbers are not only useful—they are lots of fun. Make up some fractions of your own with factorial numbers. After solving a few of them, you will be an expert.

At the Gates of Probability

Imagine that you have in your hand a bright, shiny new penny. It has no nicks or scratches and looks as if it just came from the mint. A statistician would call it a "fair" coin.

You decide to toss the penny into the air. As it rises, you wonder: Will it fall heads or tails? You know that these are the only choices—or probabilities. Since the coin is a "fair" one, it is just as likely to fall heads as tails. In statistical language, the probabilities are equal. As you continue tossing the coin, your curiosity is aroused. You decide to keep a record of how many times heads and tails have come up. You may not be aware of it, but if you do this, you are performing one of the basic experiments in probability.

If you tossed the coin ten times, these are all the possible results:

10 heads and 0 tails
9 heads and 1 tail
8 heads and 2 tails
7 heads and 3 tails
6 heads and 4 tails
5 heads and 5 tails
4 heads and 6 tails
3 heads and 7 tails
2 heads and 8 tails
1 head and 9 tails
0 heads and 10 tails

Is one of these combinations more probable than any other? Which is the most probable? Suppose that your teacher told everyone in the class to toss a coin ten times and to write down the results. What combinations would be likely to occur? If you added up all the heads and tails of the class — would there be equal numbers of each? These are questions you should start to think about. We will soon learn how to find out.

If you toss ten coins into the air at once, instead of one coin ten times, the probabilities (the combinations of heads and tails) are exactly the same.

The penny, it was said, should be a "fair" coin. Of course, most pennies are. They are just as likely to fall heads as tails. Because a coin has an equal chance of falling either way, we can predict how it will fall in a great many tosses. If the coin were damaged so that it was likely to fall heads more often than tails, we could *not* predict how it would fall.

This may seem strange, or contradictory. But, with a damaged coin, we would first have to learn about its behavior. If we tossed it 1,000 times, we might end up with 600 heads and 400 tails. We could then say that the coin would probably fall heads 6 times out of 10. But we could still not predict its behavior as accurately as we could that of a fair coin.

The law of averages

Suppose that you have tossed a fair coin into the air ten times and each time it has fallen heads. What is the probability of getting a head on the next toss? If some friends were watching you, one of them would almost certainly say, "You're bound to get a tail. The law of averages will catch up with you." The fact of the matter is that you are not "bound" to get a tail. The chance (or probability) is *exactly even* that you will get another head. On any one toss, a head is as likely as a tail, *no matter what has happened before.* In this sense, there is no such thing as the "law of averages."

Try to forget old ideas. Think this problem through clearly. You toss the coin into the air for the eleventh time. It has reached its high point and is about to fall. Does the coin "remember" that it has already fallen heads ten times in a row? Of course not! Can the coin decide how it will come down? How it fell before has nothing to do with how it will fall now. Statisticians often say, "The coin has no memory."

The toss of a coin is called an *independent event.* Nothing outside itself can influence the way it lands. The only way we can "predict" its fall is through the laws of probability. And from these laws, we know that on each toss of a coin, the probability of a head or tail is exactly equal, no matter what has happened before.

If the chances of a head or tail are exactly equal, then this should be true of a great many tosses. If you toss a coin 100 times, you should get 50 heads and 50 tails. This is theoretically true. That is, in an ideal situation this would be true. (Actually, as we shall see, there is seldom an equal division of heads and tails.)

However, if we accept this as true, what happens if we start out by getting 10 heads in a row? How will the score even out? Does it mean that we are "bound" to get 10 tails in a row to balance the 10 heads? Again, we are not "bound" to get anything. We may get 10 tails in a row. But we may also never get more than 2 tails in a row. The outstanding American probabilist, Professor William Feller, explains the evening-out process very simply. He says that the 10 heads in a row will probably be "swamped" by more tails than heads in future tosses. In other words, as we continue tossing, little by little, tails will draw even with heads. This may be what follows the "run" of 10 heads:

								Total
Heads	10	1	1	2	1	1	1	17
Tails		1	2	3	3	2	3	2	16

Despite the "run" of 10 heads, tails have almost drawn even. The "run" of 10 was never approached; it was simply swamped.

We may see this more clearly by an example from baseball, although baseball scoring does not follow these laws of probability. Let us say that the visiting team has scored 10 runs in its first inning. Does the home team also have to score 10 runs in an inning to tie the score or go ahead? Of course not. It can chip away at the lead (the visitors may still score) with 2 runs in one inning, 1 run in another, and so on, until the other team's lead has been whittled away.

Despite the "run of 10," this may be the final score:

										Final score
Visitors	10	1	0	1	2	0	1	0	0	15
Home team	1	0	2	3	0	3	2	3	2	16

The home team never even came close to the "run of 10"; the "run" was simply swamped.

The importance of a coin

The probability is very great that you will take a course in statistics if you go to college. In that event, your textbook or reference books will almost certainly discuss coin-tossing. Your first exercise in probability may be a coin-tossing experiment.

You may wonder why so much time is spent on the toss of a coin. It is only because this simple action is a perfect example, a model, of two important ideas. They are:

1. A truly *independent event.*
2. A situation with two equal probabilities.

It goes without saying that statisticians don't spend their time tossing coins, but they imagine the results of coin-tossing experiments. From these imaginings, they can make models or mathematical formulas that will help them solve real problems.

For its own sake, it is not very important whether a coin falls heads or tails. But there are really important events that follow the pattern of a tossed coin. For example, of the babies born next year, how many will be girls? An atomic particle in a chamber can move to left or right. On which side will it be? A circuit is set to open and close continuously. Will it be open or closed at a given instant? Many problems follow a pattern of "yes-no," "stop-go," "open-closed," with each choice independent of what happened before. In other words, the probabilities are limited to 1 of 2, with either one equally likely. To be able to predict what will happen in such cases, we spend time finding out how a coin will fall.

Dependent Events

Until now we have spoken of independent events, those whose outcome is not influenced by what happened before. As you may have guessed, a dependent event is influenced by, or depends upon, what you did before.

Let us imagine that you have 20 shiny marbles, or migs, or agates — whatever they may be called in your neighborhood. Of the twenty, 19 are of the familiar shiny blue-green kind. One of them is bright red. However, it is of the same size and "feel" as all the others.

You place all 20 marbles in a metal can. Without peeking, you try to pick out the red one. What is the probability? Since there are 20 in all and only 1 red one, the probability is 1 of 20. On your first try, you fail. You pick an ordinary blue-green one. Without replacing the one you picked, you try again. What is the probability of picking the red one now? Obviously, you now have a better chance. The probability is 1 of 19. Once you pick the red one, the game is over. But, otherwise, as you proceed, the probability of picking the red one becomes higher and higher — if you *do not replace* the blue-green marbles.

Each probability is dependent upon the events that happened before.

Should you fail to pick the red one on 19 consecutive attempts, what is the probability on the twentieth attempt? Obviously, there is no probability; there is only certainty. And probability, as was said earlier, deals only with uncertainty.

Combinations and Permutations

Bill and Jill, two six-year-old friends, are walking along a street. They have a penny that they can't wait to spend. In front of a candy store, they see a jelly-bean machine. Without a moment's hesitation, they run to the machine, deposit the penny, and turn the knob. Into each hand, in turn, drops a white, a red, and a black jelly bean.

Bill is an impatient boy. He has already waited too long for his treat. The colors of the jelly beans may interest him, but he won't delay his pleasure to study them. He puts all the jelly beans into his mouth, where they become one mass of jelly bean.

He ate his jelly beans as a *combination*. A combination, the dictionary says, is a group of things combined into a whole *without regard to the order of arrangement*. There is only one possible combination of 3 jelly beans eaten 3 at a time.

Jill is a girl who enjoys even the thought of eating jelly beans. She looks with delight at the lovely colors and wonders which to eat first. The red? Maybe. The white? A good idea. A bright girl, she figures out all possible arrangements of jelly-bean eating. These are the possible arrangements she has to choose from:

> white, red, black
> white, black, red
> red, white, black
> red, black, white
> black, white, red
> black, red, white

Jill made all possible *permutations* of 3 jelly beans of different colors, eaten one at a time. For her, the order was important. *Permutations* are the different arrangements that can be made from a set of things *where the order is important*.

A *combination* of things has to do with the way in which we *mix* them.

A *permutation* of things has to do with the order in which we *arrange* them.

Exactly which permutation Jill ate will remain forever a mystery. She kept the jelly beans tightly clutched in her hand. She was afraid that Bill, having eaten his, would ask her for one.

As you can see from this little story, combinations and permutations have to do with making arrangements of things. In combinations, the order is of no importance. In permutations, the order is the important thing.

Imagine that you have 3 textbooks—a history, a science, and a mathematics book. You have to place them between two bookends. If you don't care about the order, you may simply put the books between them and let it go at that. You will then have a combination of 3 books.

But suppose the order of arrangement is important to you. (You may have to pick out a book in the dark.) How many arrangements are possible? Math first because it is the thickest? Science first because it is the tallest? Alphabetical order? As with the jelly beans, there are 6 possible permutations of 3 books arranged in sets of 3.

The idea of a combination is easily understood, but let us look at one more set of permutations where the order is really important.

Jim Hanson is the track coach at Plainsville High School. For the district track meet, he has to form a 4-man relay team to compete in the 220-yard relay race. Four boys—Art, Ben, Cal, and Dan are his best sprinters. He decides that they will make up his relay team, but in what order should he place them? Who will lead off? Who will be the anchor man? He knows that the race will be close. With the best arrangement, his team has

POSSIBLE ARRANGEMENTS (PERMUTATIONS)
OF 4-MAN RELAY TEAMS

Possible arrangements
of a relay team
with Cal as starter

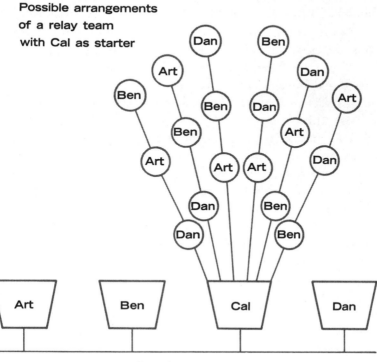

Possible starters

a chance to win. If he makes a mistake in his choices, the team may lose. He will have let his boys down by not making the best use of their talents. How many different relay teams can he make?

Very often, mathematicians use a type of illustration called a "tree" design to show all possible permutations. It is called a "tree" simply because it looks like a flowering tree with branches.

The figure above shows the number of relay teams that can be formed from 4 boys. The illustration shows clearly that Coach Hanson had to choose from 24 possible relay teams.

There are 6 teams with Cal as lead-off man. With 4 possible lead-off men, the coach can make 24 different relay teams.

In other words, there are 24 permutations (or arrangements) of 4 things taken 4 at a time.

At this point you may be thinking: Figuring out combinations and permutations may be fun, but why is it so important?

This is a subject of the greatest importance to many scientific fields. Physics, geology, and genetics are only a few examples. Let us look at genetics, or the science of the heredity of living things.

You may know that the physical characteristics of living things are controlled by the arrangement of long chains of genes, called chromosomes, which come from the parents. These cell-like chemical combinations determine whether we will have brown hair, like our mother's, or black hair, like our father's. They set the pattern for how tall we will grow. The possible combinations and permutations of these genes and chromosomes are what determine the make-up of the offspring, whether a human being, a monkey, or a plant.

Scientists have recently discovered the chemicals that carry the genetic information. So far, no attempts have been made to tamper with human heredity, but, some day, it may become possible to eliminate certain hereditary diseases.

However, the science of genetics is important in studying all living things. To come back more directly to our subject, we find that combinations and permutations are very important to a man trying to improve the milk-giving of a breed of cows; to someone working with hybrid corn; to a breeder trying to develop a larger and sweeter strawberry; to an agricultural expert trying to develop a hen that will lay more eggs.

A knowledge of combinations and permutations is of importance in government and business. Here are two examples.

In a certain state, the Motor Vehicle Commissioner has to provide license plates for 1,000,000 cars. The license plate should have as few letters and numerals as possible. This will make it cheaper to produce. There should be a sensible arrangement of the letters and numerals. This will make it easier to recognize and remember in an emergency. How many letters and numerals must he use? In this situation, he would calculate the permutations. Order is important. ABC on a license plate is different from CBA.

A businessman operates a soda fountain at which he sells 20 flavors of ice cream. With each sundae, he gives 2 scoops of ice cream. How many different sundaes can he advertise that he makes? In this case, the owner would calculate the combinations. To most people it is not important whether the vanilla or chocolate ice cream goes into the dish first.

Combination analysis plays an important part in the design of telephone trunk lines. The paths that information may take through a computer are often calculated on the basis of various combinations.

On page 95 are illustrations taken from the *Journal of Research and Development* (November 1960) of the International Business Machine Corporation (IBM). They were used to illustrate very advanced mathematical discussions having to do with combinations.

A set is a collection of objects, or observations, *considered together* for some purpose. Each object or observation in it is defined as an *element* of the set.

Knowing the number of possible arrangements of a set is important for two reasons. First, there are times when we have to know the actual number of combinations or permutations. The limits of an experiment or the design of a piece of equipment may depend upon it. Second, if we calculate the actual number of combinations or permutations, we know the probability of getting exactly the one we want, if that is our aim.

Calculating your C's and P's

Up to this point we have seen how combinations (*C*'s) and permutations (*P*'s) are made from small sets of things. One way is to list all the arrangements (ABC, ACB, etc.). Another way is by means of a tree design. But suppose you tried to make a tree design of the permutations of the 52 cards in a deck of playing cards? You would have to use the main street of your town or city as a blackboard!

We need general equations (or formulas) to help us find the number of *C*'s and *P*'s of any set, no matter how large. The equation should work whether we use all the elements of the set *or a number of them less than the total.*

Combinations (C)

The equation for finding all possible combinations of a set is

$$n\, C\, r = \frac{n!}{r!\,(n-r)!}$$

COMBINATIONS: THE NUMBER THAT CAN BE
MADE FROM n THINGS TAKEN r AT A TIME

The number of
possible combinations

The factorial value of
the number in the set

$$n C r = \frac{n!}{r!\,(n\text{-}r)!}$$

The number of
things in the set

The factorial value of the
difference between the
number in the set and the
number we will use in our
combinations

The number of things
(from the set) that we will
use in our combinations

The factorial value of
the number we will use
in our combinations

This is how to read the formula:

1. (The left side): The number of combinations (C) that can be made from a set of *n* things taken *r* at a time is equal to

2. (The right side): *n* factorial divided by *r* factorial times $(n - r)$ factorial.

This is what the parts of the formula stand for:

n   The number of things in the set. (If the set were the alphabet, *n* would equal 26, the total number of letters of the alphabet.)

C   The number of all possible combinations that can be made.

r   The number of elements, or things, that we will use in making our combinations. (If we were making 5-letter combinations from the letters of the alphabet, *r* would equal 5.)

n!   The factorial value of the number of things in the set. (For the letters of the alphabet, *n!* would be equal to 26!)

r!   The factorial value of the number of things we will use in making our combinations. (In the above example, it would be 5!).

$(n - r)!$ The factorial value of the difference between the number of things in the set and the number we will use in making our combinations. (In the above example, it would be $(26 - 5)!$ or 21!)

(*Note:* The number of ways in which *r* objects can be selected from a set of *n* is frequently shown as $\binom{n}{r}$. For clarity in this beginners' probability section, we will continue to show it as *n C r*.)

Equations always seem much more complicated in explanations than they are in use. This one is a good example. Let us apply it to jelly-bean eating and see how simple it really is.

We already know that 3 jelly beans, eaten 3 at a time, result in only 1 combination. The equation should prove this. (*Reminder:* 0! = 1. For other factorial values, see the table on page 68.)

PROBLEM: *How many combinations can be made from 3 jelly beans, eaten 3 at a time?*

Use the formula

$$n\,C\,r = \frac{n!}{r!\,(n-r)!}$$

In this problem, $n = 3$ (for the entire set of 3 jelly beans); $r = 3$ (since we will use all 3 jelly beans in making our combinations); $(n - r)! = 0!$ (since $(3 - 3) = 0$). Therefore

$$3\,C\,3 = \frac{3!}{3!(3-3)!} = \frac{3!}{3! \times 0!} = \frac{6}{6 \times 1} = \frac{6}{6} = 1$$

(*Note:* We could substitute 1 for the 3! in the numerator and denominator. In later problems we will use this shortcut.)

We would read our answer as follows: The number of combinations (*C*) that can be made from 3 things, taken 3 at a time, is 1.

PROBLEM: *How many combinations can be made from 3 jelly beans, eaten 2 at a time?*

$$3\,C\,2 = \frac{3!}{2!(3-2)!} = \frac{3!}{2! \times 1!} = \frac{6}{2 \times 1} = \frac{6}{2} = 3$$

From a set of 3, we can make 3 combinations—if we combine only 2 things at a time. Using red, white, and black, the combinations would be

red, white
red, black
white, black

With this simple formula, we can solve many problems. But problem-solving requires more than the use of a formula for automatic results. It requires thought. We should always ask ourselves these two questions:

1. Have I used the formula correctly?
2. Have I solved the problem?

Just as your mother seasons meat with salt, so should you "season" the formulas with a liberal sprinkling of common sense. Take this as a warning that some of the problems may have a "catch" to them.

PROBLEM 1: *A father takes his son to a store to buy him some ties. He tells him, "Son, choose any 3 ties that you like." The boy finds 10 ties that appeal to him. From these, he must choose 3.*

Order is not important since he will walk out of the store with a 3-tie combination.

How many different combinations must he choose from?

$$10 \ C \ 3 = \frac{10!}{3!(10-3)!} = \frac{10!}{3! \times 7!} = \frac{10 \times 9 \times 8 \times 7!}{3! \times 7!}$$

$$= \frac{10 \times 9 \times 8}{3!} = \frac{720}{6} = 120$$

(REMINDER: 10! is the same as $10 \times 9 \times 8 \times 7!$ Therefore, we can substitute 1 for the 7! in the numerator and denominator.)

There are no "catches." The boy has to choose from 120 possible combinations. If his father were a mathematician, he would be very patient with him.

PROBLEM 2: *A mother and daughter visit a department store. The girl has been told that she may select 2 summer and 2 winter dresses. After going through all the dress racks, mother and daughter are carrying 5 possible summer and 5 possible winter dresses. If we assume that her choice of summer dresses has nothing to do with her choice of winter dresses, how many combinations to choose from now face the girl?*

Since one has nothing to do with the other, we can break up the problem into two parts. Starting with the summer dresses,

$$5 \ C \ 2 = \frac{5!}{2!(5-2)!} = \frac{5!}{2! \times 3!} = \frac{5 \times 4 \times 3!}{2! \times 3!} = \frac{5 \times 4}{2!} = \frac{20}{2} = 10$$

After making her selection from 10 possible combinations of summer dresses, the girl will face the same problem with the winter ones.

Since one set has nothing to do with the other, we add the combinations. Therefore, she has 20 combinations (10 + 10) from which to choose.

(*Note:* The adding of probabilities will be dealt with much more fully in a later section.)

PROBLEM 3: *It is now time for some refreshment. Let's visit our old friend who runs the soda fountain. He is still featuring 20 flavors of ice cream. And you may still choose, if you wish, 2 flavors with your sundae. To attract customers, he places the following ad in the local newspaper:*

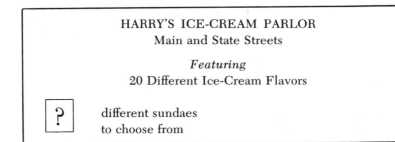

HARRY'S ICE-CREAM PARLOR
Main and State Streets

Featuring
20 Different Ice-Cream Flavors

? different sundaes
to choose from

What numeral can he honestly use in the box?

a. *The combinations of 2 different flavors from 20:*

$$20 \ C \ 2 = \frac{20!}{2!(20-2)!} = \frac{20!}{2! \times 18!} = \frac{20 \times 19 \times 18!}{2! \times 18!}$$

$$= \frac{20 \times 19}{2!} = \frac{380}{2} = 190$$

He can make 190 different sundaes if you choose 2 *different* flavors.

But what about the boy who loves pistachio so much that he can't bear any other flavor on his plate? He calls for an all-pistachio sundae.

b. *The addition of the 20 flavors:*

To the 190 combinations of 2 different flavors, we must add 20 flavors for those who say, "All chocolate, please!" or, "Make mine all strawberry!" Therefore, Harry can put 210 (190 + 20) in the box and be an honest businessman.

PROBLEM 4: *Coach Frank Dribble and his assistant look at the 10 boys who have come out for the school's basketball team. The coach will use them all, but he wants the 5 best players for the regular team.*

His assistant suggests, "Why not let 2 teams play against each other? Try out every combination and let the top-scoring team be our regulars."

Coach Dribble, who also happens to be a mathematics teacher, looks at him, amazed. "Do you realize how many games we would have to watch?"

Well, how many games would they have to watch?

The combination of 5 boys (a basketball team) from a group of 10:

$$10 \ C \ 5 = \frac{10!}{5!(10-5)!} = \frac{10!}{5! \times 5!} = \frac{10 \times 9 \times 8 \times 7 \times 6}{5!} = \frac{30,240}{120} = 252$$

There are 252 combinations of teams of 5.

The number of games to watch:

Since the 10 boys are divided into 2 combinations of 5 every time they play, Coach Dribble and his assistant would have to watch 126 *games* (252/2).

The coach picked his team some other way. Otherwise, the basketball season would have ended before he had made his choice.

Before moving on to permutations, we will consider one more problem. It is a very simple one. The numbers are very large, but there are no "catches." It has to do with a simple gambling game. Since gamblers were the first to make use of probability, it takes us back to our beginnings.

More important than this, it is a problem with a moral.

PROBLEM 5: *Poker is a game that any child can learn in 10 minutes. Children, as well as gamblers, find it fascinating. It is played with a regular deck of 52 cards. Each player is dealt 5 cards. From this point on, it can be played in many different ways. Some parts of the United States have one set of rules; other parts, other rules.*

The player who holds the best cards, according to the rules, wins the hand. The game holds its attraction because of the tremendous number of possible hands. How many different 5-card poker hands can be dealt from a deck of 52 cards? (No two cards are alike.)

$$52 \ C \ 5 = \frac{52!}{5!(52-5)!} = \frac{52!}{5! \times 47!} = \frac{52 \times 51 \times 50 \times 49 \times 48}{5!}$$

$$= \frac{311{,}875{,}200}{120} = 2{,}598{,}960$$

What happened to the 47! in the numerator and denominator?

There are more than 2½ million different hands. If a player were dealt 100 poker hands every day of the year, he could play for more than 70 years without holding the same hand twice.

The best hand in poker is generally considered to be a royal flush in spades. It consists of the following cards: ace, king, queen, jack, and ten. The probability of being dealt this combination is exactly 1 out of 2,598,960.

A worthless hand might consist of the following cards: 3 of clubs, 4 of hearts, 6 of diamonds, 7 of clubs, and 9 of hearts. The probability of being dealt this hand is also exactly 1 out of 2,598,960.

The player who held the first hand would consider himself extremely lucky; the player holding the second hand would consider himself extremely unlucky. But, before any card is dealt, each hand is equally probable.

The moral of the story is this: We must never confuse probability with desirability.

Permutations (P)

Problems requiring the use of permutations of one kind or another are very common in the sciences. In scientific investigations, the order of arrangement, or happening, is often important.

We already know that the rearrangement of sets of things will result in more permutations than combinations. The 3 jelly beans gave us 1 combination but 6 permutations.

By placing the two equations together, we can see how they are alike and how they differ.

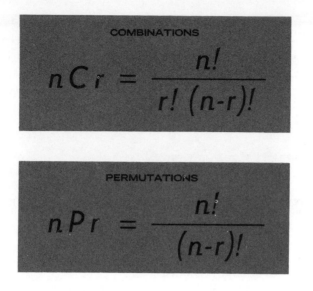

In the permutation equation, we have removed $r!$ from the denominator. As a result, our numerator will be divided by a smaller number, making the answer larger. The answer is larger by a factor of $r!$.

In other words, if we divide the number of permutations by the value of $r!$, we know the number of combinations — *provided that we use the same number of things from the same set.*

This is shown very clearly by the jelly-bean example.

Combinations

$$3\, C\, 3 = \frac{3!}{3!(3-3)!} = \frac{6}{6 \times 1} = 1$$

Permutations

$$3\, P\, 3 = \frac{3!}{(3-3)!} = \frac{6}{0!} = \frac{6}{1} = 6$$

We see that the number of permutations is exactly $r!$ (which, in this case, is $3! = 6$) times as great as the number of combinations.

By the use of the tree design, we saw that it was possible to make 24 different relay teams from 4 sprinters. The equation for permutations should give us the same result:

$$n \, P \, r = \frac{n!}{(n-r)!}$$

Therefore:

$$4 \, P \, 4 = \frac{4!}{(4-4)!} = \frac{4!}{0!} = \frac{24}{1} = 24$$

Let us apply this useful equation to some problems. (*Remember:* We want to solve problems and not merely use the equation without thinking.)

PROBLEM 1: *Argentina, Brazil, and Chile are sometimes called the ABC countries of South America.*

The presidents of the three countries meet for a conference. The first thing they decide is the order in which their countries' flags will fly during the conference. The order in which flags are flown is considered important to a country's pride and prestige. They make the following decisions:

If all 3 are present, all flags will be flown in a different order each day.

If 1 president has to rush back home for a day, 2 flags will be flown. The order will be changed every time this happens.

Let's pretend that the conference lasts long enough for all possible arrangements to be flown. How many arrangements are possible?

3 flags flown 3 at a time:

$$3 \, P \, 3 = \frac{3!}{(3-3)!} = \frac{3!}{0!} = \frac{6}{1} = 6$$

3 flags flown 2 at a time:

$$3 \, P \, 2 = \frac{3!}{(3-2)!} = \frac{3!}{1!} = \frac{6}{1} = 6$$

Since the different sets of arrangements have nothing to do with each other (the flags may be flown by 2's *or* by 3's), we add them. There are, therefore, 6 + 6 or 12 possible arrangements.

It may surprise you that the answer is 6 arrangements of 3 things, taken 3 at a time or 2 at a time. The listing of the possible arrangements proves that this is so.

Three at a time	Two at a time
ABC	AB
ACB	AC
BAC	BA
BCA	BC
CAB	CA
CBA	CB

PROBLEM 2: *The Chunky Chewy Company has put out a new cereal called ChewChunk. To encourage people to try it, the company will send free sample coupons to 1,000 families in each state — 50,000 families altogether.*

Sooner or later, the used coupons will come back to the company from grocers and supermarkets. The company would like to know how many families in each state cash in the coupons. To find this out, it decides to print a secret code on the coupon. It keeps a record of the code numbers it sends to the states. The company decides to use 2 different letters *and* 2 different numerals *on each coupon (AA12 or GF33). Will this allow enough arrangements (permutations) for 50,000 separate codes?*

(*Reminder:* AB *12* and AB *13* are, of course, different codes.)

The 26 letters of the alphabet, used 2 at a time:

$$26 \, P \, 2 = \frac{26!}{(26-2)!} = \frac{26!}{24!} = \frac{26 \times 25 \times 24!}{24!} = \frac{26 \times 25}{1} = 650$$

There are 650 possible arrangements of 2 different letters.

The 10 digits (0 — 9), used 2 at a time:

$$10 \, P \, 2 = \frac{10!}{(10-2)!} = \frac{10!}{8!} = \frac{10 \times 9 \times 8!}{8!} = \frac{10 \times 9}{1} = 90$$

There are 90 possible arrangements of 2 different digits.

Since the letter and numeral arrangements *go together,* the totals must be multiplied. (With the flags, we could fly either 2 *or* 3.)

Therefore, with 2 different letters and 2 different digits used to-gether, we have: $650 \times 90 = 58,500$ possible arrangements, or per-mutations.

There will be more than enough for 50,000 coupons. You will see the reason for multiplying the letter total by the digit total if you pic-ture it in this way: We use AB *01*, AB *02*, AB *03*, etc., until the entire 90 numeral arrangements are used up with the AB's. Then, we start again with AC *01*, AC *02*, AC *03*, etc.

Up to this point, the sets we arranged were made up of elements (things) that were different. The letters of the alpha-bet differ from one another. So do the cards in a deck. So did the flavors of ice cream.

Now we will consider problems where the elements of the set are not all different.

PROBLEM 3: *The puzzle page of many newspapers often has an* ana-gram, *particularly in weekend editions. In an anagram, the letters of a word are scrambled. The reader solves the anagram by arranging the letters in their correct order so that they spell out the actual word. For example,* TTTAIICSSS *is one possible anagram for* STATISTICS.

Although it may not seem so, in an anagram, order is important. The best possible order is the one that will keep the reader busy for the longest time. An anagram is nothing more than 1 permutation of the letters in the word. By use of the equation we have been using for permutations, we can find out how many anagrams can be made from a word—if all the letters in the word are different.

a. How many anagrams can be made from the word SPHINX?

Since all the letters are different, we can use the permutation formula for 6 things, used 6 at a time:

$$6\,P\,6 = \frac{6!}{(6-6)!} = \frac{6!}{0!} = \frac{720}{1} = 720$$

But now suppose that we have to handle a hot potato like the word POTATO? Here, the letters are not all different.

By changing our equation slightly, we can handle such problems. The equation in such cases is

$$n P_{r_1 r_2 r_3}, etc. = \frac{n!}{r_1!\; r_2!\; r_3!\,, etc.}$$

We read r_1, r_2, r_3 as r one, r two, r three. We use as many as we need. Each different element of the set has its own r number.

Let us analyze the word POTATO:

Letters in the word	Number of times each occurs	The r number to be used
O	2	r_1
T	2	r_2
A	1	r_3
P	1	r_4
	6 [= n (or the number of letters in the word)]	

It doesn't matter which letter becomes r_1, r_2, r_3, or r_4. The result will always be the same.

b. How many anagrams can be made from the word POTATO?

$$n P\, r_1\, r_2\, r_3\, r_4 = \frac{n!}{r_1!\; r_2!\; r_3!\; r_4!}$$

$$6\, P\, 2\, 2\, 1\, 1 = \frac{6!}{2! \times 2! \times 1! \times 1!} = \frac{720}{2 \times 2 \times 1 \times 1} = \frac{720}{4} = 180$$

From SPHINX we were able to make 720 anagrams; from POTATO, only 180. This leads us to an important observation.

The more the elements of a set are alike, the smaller the number of possible arrangements. If you think about it, it will seem perfectly reasonable. In POTATO, the letters TT and OO cannot be rearranged. They really represent one unit. They become different only if we attach labels to them or write them in different colored ink.

To prove the above point we will use another 6-letter word in which the elements (the letters) are even more alike.

c. *How many anagrams can be made from the word* TEEPEE?

E has a frequency of $4 = r_1$
T has a frequency of $1 = r_2$
P has a frequency of $1 = r_3$

$$6\ P\ 4\ 1\ 1 = \frac{6!}{4! \times 1! \times 1!} = \frac{720}{24 \times 1 \times 1} = \frac{720}{24} = 30$$

When you go to a movie, you may hiss the villain by making a sound like SSSSSS. Can you make an anagram from this 6-letter hiss? Of course not! No matter how you arrange it, a hiss is still a hiss. This brings up an important point about problem-solving.

All our possible anagram totals (720, 180, 30) have to be reduced by 1. If anagrams are scrambled letters of words, would you use the word itself (SPHINX, POTATO, TEEPEE) as an anagram? Of course not! But the word itself is one of the possible arrangements, or permutations, of the letters!

(*Remember:* An equation is a tool. It is never a substitute for thinking.)

There is one other type of permutation problem that is both useful and interesting. It has to do with putting things that are all alike into different boxes, or containers. The problem usually is: In how many different ways can this be done?

We will see this clearly in the following problem.

PROBLEM 4: *Helen had some of her friends visit her. She served them her mother's home-baked cookies and lemonade. After they left, her mother said, "Helen, please put the left-over cookies away." There were 8 cookies to be put away. They were, of course, all alike. The family (it's a large one) has 3 cookie jars. In how many different ways could Helen have distributed them among the 3 jars?*

To enable you to "see" the problem, all possible arrangements are shown on the next page. We will call the cookie jars *A*, *B*, and *C*.

There are, altogether, 45 different ways of putting 8 cookies into 3 jars.

We want to avoid having to make long lists of the possibilities. What if electrons are involved? We would run short of paper!

	Jar A	Jar B	Jar C
All 8	8	0	0
in 1	0	8	0
jar	0	0	8
	7	0	1
	7	1	0
	0	7	1
7 in	1	7	0
1 jar	0	1	7
	1	0	7
	6	0	2
	6	1	1
	6	2	0
	0	6	2
6 in	1	6	1
1 jar	2	6	0
	0	2	6
	1	1	6
	2	0	6

	Jar A	Jar B	Jar C
	5	0	3
	5	1	2
	5	2	1
	5	3	0
5 in	0	5	3
1 jar	1	5	2
	2	5	1
	3	5	0
	0	3	5
	1	2	5
	2	1	5
	3	0	5

	Jar A	Jar B	Jar C
	4	0	4
	4	1	3
No more	4	2	2
than 4	4	3	1
in 1 jar	4	4	0
	0	4	4
	1	4	3
	2	4	2
	3	4	1
	1	3	4
	2	2	4
	3	1	4
No more	3	2	3
than 3	3	3	2
in 1 jar	2	3	3

Here is a simple formula which we can apply to the same problem:

$$\frac{\text{The number of ways in which identical things can be placed into different containers}}{} = \frac{(r+n-1)!}{(r-1)!\,n!}$$

This is what the n and r stand for: $n =$ The number of things that are identical (the same) and that are to be distributed. $r =$ The number of different containers.

Using the formula in our cookie problem, we have $n = 8$ cookies, all alike; $r = 3$ separate cookie jars.

$$\frac{(3+8-1)!}{(3-1)!\,8!} = \frac{10!}{2! \times 8!} = \frac{10 \times 9 \times 8!}{2! \times 8!} = \frac{10 \times 9}{2!} = \frac{90}{2} = 45$$

The equation gives us the answer in a few steps.

Conclusion

The problems we have solved deal with the ordinary things that people do. But this is not the limit of the usefulness of the equations. Problems having to do with combinations and permutations arise in many forms in science and in business.

The "free coupon" problem we solved is not too different from the way such coupons are often marked. The tree diagram of the relay team is a simple model of tree diagrams dealing with the design of computers or telephone exchanges. The illustrations on the next page of tree designs that appeared in an IBM mathematical journal are good examples.

The idea of being able to put 8 cookies into 3 jars in 45 different ways may be amusing, but the *basic* problem is an important one in many fields. Below are examples, taken from a book on probability by Professor William Feller, *An Introduction to Probability Theory and Its Applications* (John Wiley and Sons), of the many kinds of problems that are solved by this method. It is not important that you understand completely each example. It is important that you realize how widely a simple model can be applied.

1. Accidents: Classifying accidents by the day of the week on which they happen.

2. Weapons firing: The number of hits made on a target.

3. Irradiation in biology: Light particles hitting the cells of the retina of the eye.

4. The genetic effects of radiation.

5. Cosmic-ray experiments: Particles hitting a Geiger counter.

6. Passengers getting off an elevator. (This is important in designing and placing elevators in skyscrapers.)

7. The distribution of genes in descendants.

8. Chemistry: Long-chain polymers reacting with oxygen.

9. Photographic emulsions: A photographic plate is covered by grains sensitive to units of light.

10. Misprints on a printed page.

The equations you have learned are simple ones. But they have many uses. An important and useful equation does not

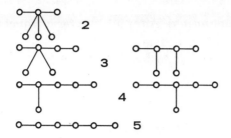

Trees with six points by diameter

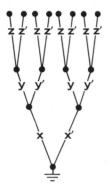

Ordinary relay tree for 3 relays

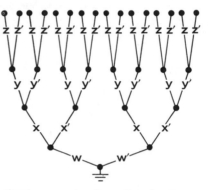

Ordinary relay tree for 4 relays

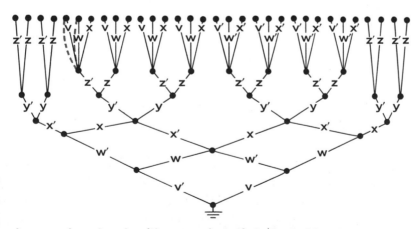

Lupanov's network with a sneak path indicated by dotted lines

(*From* Journal of Research and Development, *Vol. 4, No. 5, Novem-ber 1960, International Business Machines Corporation*)

have to be complicated. After all, the basic equation of atomic physics is Einstein's $e = mc^2$.

The main thing is to be able to see how an equation can help us solve a problem.

The Probability of an Event

Probability is a measure of the likelihood that an event will take place. It is usually shown as a fraction, somewhere between 0 and 1. The diagram below shows the limits.

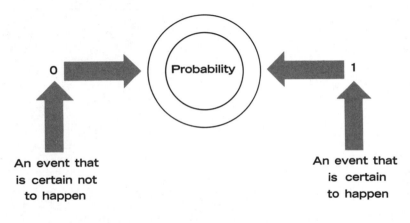

An event that is certain not to happen

An event that is certain to happen

An event that is certain not to happen may sound silly when stated. For example, the probability of getting a 7 on one toss of one ordinary die (the singular of dice) is 0.

The mathematical probability of 0 and the expressions we use in everyday conversation do not go hand-in-hand. We often say, "Oh, that's impossible!" But there may be a mathematical probability, however small, that the event may happen.

Suppose you were asked, "What is the probability that a man will live to be 300 years old?" Your immediate reply would most likely be, "Oh, that's impossible!" It's true that no record exists of anyone's having lived that long, but can you foresee the future? If you were running an insurance company, would you give away free life insurance policies to be cashed in by anyone who reaches the age of 300? What would you set as a limit on a man's life?

As a matter of fact, insurance companies have a calculated probability that a policyholder might reach that age. It is a very, very small probability, but it is not zero.

In some fields of atomic physics, probabilities of less than 1 in 1,000,000 are considered high probabilities indeed.

An event with a probability 0 must have absolutely no chance of happening.

An event that is certain to happen seems very obvious when stated. The probability of getting a head or a tail on one toss of a coin is 1. These are the only possible results. If we say "head *or* tail," we have used up all the probabilities.

This leads to the first statement about probability relationships: *The sum of all the probabilities connected with an experiment is 1.*

For example, if we toss a fair die (one of a pair of dice), each one of the 6 numbers has an equal chance of coming up (being the top face). The probabilities are:

Number on the face of the die	*Probability of being top face*
1	$\dfrac{1}{6}$
2	$\dfrac{1}{6}$
3	$\dfrac{1}{6}$
4	$\dfrac{1}{6}$
5	$\dfrac{1}{6}$
6	$\dfrac{1}{6}$

$$\text{\textit{Sum of all probabilities}} = \frac{6}{6} = 1$$

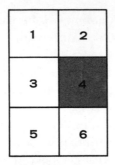

On a diagram, if we showed the area that any one face —
the 4, for example — occupied, it would be 1/6 of the total space.

Let us look at one more example.

In one school class there are 25 students. Only one of them
is a red-headed boy. The teacher has a class card for each student. She shuffles the cards and pulls out one card by chance,
not by choice.

What is the probability that it is the card of the red-headed
boy?

Since there are 25 students and there is an equal chance to
pick any card, the probability is 1/25. On a diagram, the red-
headed boy would occupy 1/25th of the space.

1	2	3	4	5
6	7	8	9	10
11	12	13	14	15
16	17	18	19	20
21	22	23	24	25

In the language of modern probability, each possible result is called a *sample point*. The total of all possible results (the sum of all sample points) is called the *sample space*.

The examples of the coin, the die, and the 25 students have this in common: *The probabilities are known in advance.* No matter what kind of problem we make up, we know that the probability of heads on the toss of a coin is 1/2; the probability of tails is 1/2. The probability of getting 4 on one toss of a die is 1/6; the probability of getting any other *one* number is also 1/6. The probability of picking out the card of the red-headed boy is 1/25; the probability of picking out the card of any other one student is also 1/25.

This kind of probability is known by the Latin words *a priori* (pronounced "ah pree-aw'-ree") probability. *A priori* simply means knowing in advance. For some time, we will be dealing with *a priori* probabilities.

The examples have another thing in common. They can be shown as a formula that would apply to all of them. We could express it in words, as follows:

$$\text{\textit{The probability of success (of getting the result we want)}} = \frac{\text{the number of equally likely ways the result can happen}}{\text{the total number of possible results}}$$

Translating this into the language of coin-tossing, we would write the following:

$$\text{\textit{The probability of success (of getting "head" if that is what we want)}} = \frac{\text{the number of equally likely ways that "head" can come up}}{\text{all possible results of tossing a coin, which are heads and tails}} = \frac{1}{2}$$

At this point, you certainly know that statisticians don't bother writing all this to express a simple idea. They use symbols. The most commonly accepted symbols to express the formula are

$$P(A) = \frac{A}{N} \leftarrow \text{\textit{the number of ways A can happen}} \\ \phantom{P(A) = \frac{A}{N}} \leftarrow \text{\textit{all possible results}}$$

This can be read as the probability of *A* happening [*P(A)*] = the number of ways in which *A* can happen, divided by all possible results (*N*).

Let's take this idea a few steps further.

We say that something (an event) can happen in *A* ways. What about the ways in which it *cannot* happen? These are usually called the *B* ways. You may already have reached the conclusion that

$$A + B = N$$

Since *A* = the ways in which an event *can* happen, *B* = the ways in which an event *cannot* happen, and *N* = all possible results, the formula

$$P(A) = \frac{A}{N}$$

may be written

$$P(A) = \frac{A}{A + B}$$

since, as stated, *N* = *A* + *B*.

PROBLEM: *Apply the formulas to the probability of a 4 coming up on 1 toss of a die.*

$$P(A) \qquad = \frac{A}{N} = \frac{1}{6} \quad \begin{array}{l} \textit{(there is only 1 way it can happen)} \\ \textit{(all possible results—the faces} \\ \qquad \textit{from 1 to 6)} \end{array}$$

(*the probability
of success—
4 coming up*)

or

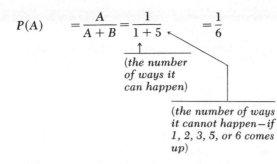

$$P(A) = \frac{A}{A+B} = \frac{1}{1+5} = \frac{1}{6}$$

(the number of ways it can happen)

(the number of ways it cannot happen — if 1, 2, 3, 5, or 6 comes up)

The probability of success [$P(A)$] in getting a 4 on 1 toss of an ordinary die is 1/6.

The probability of failure has its own symbol. Most commonly, it is written

$$Q(A) = \frac{B}{N}$$

Q represents the probability of failure — of not getting A; B represents the number of ways A cannot happen; and N represents, again, all possible results.

In trying to get a 4 on a die in 1 toss,

$$Q(A \text{ is } 4) = \frac{B}{N} = \frac{5}{6}$$

If you stop to think about it (and you should), you can readily see that:

$$P + Q = 1$$

The probability of success (P) and the probability of failure (Q) account for all probabilities. This, as was shown earlier, must equal 1.

With these simple fractions, we can find the number of successes or failures in more than one trial. We multiply the fraction by the number of trials.

PROBLEM 1: *On the average, how many times will a 4 come up in 120 tosses of a die?*

We know: $P(4) = 1/6$. We simply multiply our fraction by the number of tosses:

$$P(4, \text{ in 120 tosses}) = 120 \left(\frac{1}{6}\right) = 20$$

PROBLEM 2: *On the average, how many times will a number other than 4 come up on 120 tosses of a die?*

We know: $Q(4) = 5/6$.

$$Q(4, \text{ in 120 tosses}) = 120 \times \frac{5}{6} = \frac{600}{6} = 100$$

This is exactly what we would expect.

These simple exercises have been emphasized for a purpose. They were meant to start you thinking in terms of probability. They are also some of the basic building blocks of probability.

The terms "success" and "failure" need some explanation. Statisticians do not like the terms. Scientists using probability do not like them. But in every book on probability you will find them sooner or later.

In performing an experiment, a scientist records the results of his tests, or trials. Watching a radioactive substance break down, for example, does not involve "success" or "failure." It simply happens. The difficulty is, however, that no one has ever found substitute terms that everyone will accept. Also, these terms go far back into the history of probability. Gamblers, of course, think only in terms of success or failure.

Adding probabilities

The probability of an event is seldom as clear as it was in the examples just given. More often, probabilities clash. Events may come in bunches. Each may have a probability quite unique to itself. They then have to be added, subtracted, multiplied, or divided. After one or more of these steps have been performed, the real probability is the answer.

There are a few simple rules to help decide which steps to use. If you add to these rules a generous sprinkling of common sense, you will be able to solve many problems in probability.

> *Definition: Mutually exclusive events.* Mutually exclusive events cannot happen together or at the same time. Only *1* of *2 or more* mutually exclusive events can take place at one time, or test, or experiment.
>
> *Rule:* When 2 events are mutually exclusive and the first can happen in X number of ways and the second can happen in Y number of ways, then *one or the other* can happen in X + Y number of ways.

$$P(X \text{ or } Y) = P(X) + P(Y)$$

What is the probability of getting a 4 *or* a 5 on 1 toss of a die? Since the probability of 4 is 1/6th, and of 5 also 1/6th, the probability of one *or* the other is the sum of the probabilities, or $1/6 + 1/6 = 1/3$. If you look back at the simple die-tossing diagram and fill in the box for number 5, it is obvious that 2 of the 6 possible spaces will be filled.

PROBLEM 1: *Your school has 2 free passes to give away for its next football game. The 10 best students will compete for them. To give each one a fair chance, 10 slips, numbered 0 to 9, are folded. Each student has 1 pick. It is decided that 3 and 7 will be the winning numbers. What is the probability of winning a pass?*

The probability of picking number 3 is 1/10, since there are 10 digits and each student has 1 pick. The probability of picking number 7 is also 1/10. Therefore, the probability of picking a winning number (3 *or* 7) is

$$\frac{1}{10} + \frac{1}{10} = \frac{2}{10} = \frac{1}{5}$$

(*Note:* You will see later that there is no advantage in being either the first or last student to take a pick. The order does not affect the probability.)

You may have been able to solve the problem by logic, that is, by reasoning it out. The next problem should present no greater difficulty. There are only more elements involved.

PROBLEM 2: *A new gasoline station has opened in your neighborhood. To attract customers, it offers a* choice *of 4 free gifts. They are:*

1. *A set of drinking glasses*
2. *A pair of nylon stockings*
3. *A ball-point pen and pencil set*
4. *A beach bag*

The first 100 customers made these choices:

$$\begin{array}{rl} 50 & \textit{chose the drinking glasses} \\ 25 & \textit{chose the stockings} \\ 15 & \textit{chose the pen and pencil set} \\ \underline{10} & \textit{chose the beach bag} \\ \overline{100} & \end{array}$$

We will assume that this is a pattern that future customers will follow. What is the probability that a customer will choose stockings or a pen set?

(*Note:* Do not reduce fraction to the lowest denominator until the last step. In other words, your denominator should be 100 until then.)

The probabilities are set by changing the number of choices into fractions of 100 — the total number of customers. Therefore, the probability of choosing:

$$\begin{array}{ll} \text{glasses} & = 50/100 \\ \text{stockings} & = 25/100 \\ \text{pen} & = 15/100 \\ \text{bag} & = 10/100 \end{array}$$

The probability of any customer's choosing stockings (X) or a pen set (Y) is

$$P(X \text{ or } Y) = \frac{25}{100} + \frac{15}{100} = \frac{40}{100} = \frac{2}{5}$$

You can, of course, calculate the probability of any combination.

The calculations in such problems are not complicated. The choices are clear-cut. But, sometimes, probabilities overlap. There are elements with the character of X; there are others with the character of Y. But there are also elements with the character of X and Y.

As an example, suppose we asked: What is the probability that an American home has a television or a hi-fi (high fidelity) set? As you probably know, many homes have both. How do we take these into account?

The problem may be seen more clearly by means of a Venn diagram. This type of diagram was developed by John Venn, an English logician (one specializing in logical thinking) of the nineteenth century.

The diagram on page 106 shows that we cannot merely add X and Y. This would mean including XY twice. Since we want to know about families who own *either* a TV set *or* a hi-fi set, we must subtract the value of XY from the probability $X + Y$. XY is part of both circles.

To eliminate the value of XY, once, we change our probability formula slightly. Now

$$P(X \text{ or } Y) = P(X) + P(Y) - P(XY)$$

If you analyze the formula, you will note that one can use it even when probabilities do not overlap. In that case, the value of $P(XY)$ would be 0, and we would be back at our starting point.

PROBLEM: *A statistician in Certain City has been asked to determine the probability that students are taking music* or *dancing lessons. He finds the results of a survey by the United Dancing Teachers that shows that 1 child in 50 is taking dancing lessons. Another survey, by the Music Teachers of Certain City, shows that 1 child in 25 receives music lessons.*

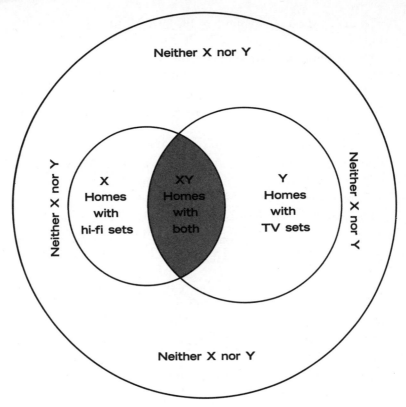

He suspects that some students take both music and dancing lessons. He therefore makes his own survey. The results show that 1 student in 100 takes lessons in both.

What is, then, the probability that a student is taking either music or dancing lessons?

The statistician has the following information:

1. Probability of music lessons   = 1/25 (let music   = X)
2. Probability of dancing lessons = 1/50 (let dancing = Y)
3. Probability of both   = 1/100 (XY)

Since

$$P(X \text{ or } Y) = P(X) + P(Y) - P(XY)$$

then

$$P(X \text{ or } Y) = \frac{1}{25} + \frac{1}{50} - \frac{1}{100}$$

To simplify matters, change all fractions to a common denominator of 100:

$$P(X \text{ or } Y) = \frac{4}{100} + \frac{2}{100} - \frac{1}{100} = \frac{5}{100} = \frac{1}{20}$$

The probability is 1 out of 20, therefore, that a student picked by chance is taking either music or dancing lessons. If you tried to form a school orchestra from students picked by chance, only 1 out of 20 would probably have had training in music or rhythm.

Things begin to get really complicated when three probabilities are competing for our attention — and they all overlap! But John Venn, with his logical diagrams, comes to our assistance again.

PROBLEM: *What is the probability that a college student participates in baseball, basketball, or football? We realize at once that there will be some who participate in two sports, but there are also those all-around athletes who compete in all three. How do we handle them?*
As a first step, let us list all the possibilities:

1. Baseball only   (X)
2. Basketball only   (Y)
3. Football only   (Z)
4. Baseball and basketball   (XY)
5. Baseball and football   (XZ)
6. Basketball and football   (YZ)
7. All three   (XYZ)

The ones who don't participate in any of these sports complete our probabilities.
This is what our diagram would show:

A VENN DIAGRAM WHEN THERE ARE: X XY
Y XZ XYZ
Z YZ

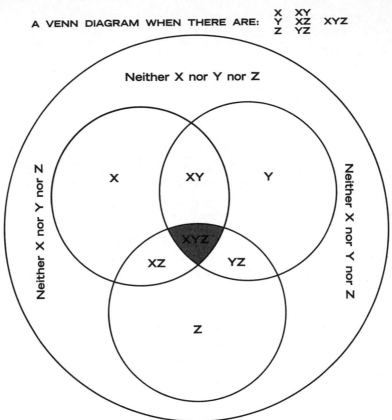

The formula for a situation such as this is

$$P(X \text{ or } Y \text{ or } Z) = P(X) + P(Y) + P(Z) - P(XY) - P(XZ)$$
$$- P(YZ) + P(XYZ)$$

Up to the point where we *add* the probability of XYZ, the formula does not differ from the previous one. It has only more elements.

If you are puzzled as to why XYZ must be added, let's examine what happened to it in the process of adding and subtracting the other probabilities:

It was added as part of X, as part of Y, as part of Z.	It was subtracted as part of XY, as part of XZ, as part of YZ.

Since it was added 3 times and subtracted 3 times, it was really left out in the cold. Therefore, we have to account for it somehow. We do it by adding it at the end of the formula.

PROBLEM: *A student is asked to write a term paper about American farms. One of the questions he has to answer is this: What is the probability that an American commercial farm raises corn or wheat or rye? (He could be asked: What proportion of —?)*

He goes to the library and looks through publications of the U.S. Department of Agriculture. Luckily, he finds exactly what he is looking for. On one page there is a table with the following information:

Principal Farm Crops
1 out of 8 farms grows corn
1 out of 10 farms grows wheat
1 out of 25 farms grows rye

On another page he finds this table:

Two Principal Crops on Farms Growing
Two Crops or More
1 out of 25 farms grows corn and wheat
1 out of 50 farms grows corn and rye
1 out of 100 farms grows wheat and rye

On still another page, in a story about farms, he finds this phrase, "1 out of 200 farms grows corn, wheat, and rye."

Now the student has only to put all the information together and apply it to his formula.

(*Note:* The above statistics are purely imaginary. Actually, about 1 out of 6 American commercial farms raises grain crops.)

Let

$$
\begin{aligned}
\text{corn} &= X = 1/8 \\
\text{wheat} &= Y = 1/10 \\
\text{rye} &= Z = 1/25 \\
\\
\text{corn and wheat} &= XY = 1/25 \\
\text{corn and rye} &= XZ = 1/50 \\
\text{wheat and rye} &= YZ = 1/100 \\
\\
\text{corn, wheat, and rye} &= XYZ = 1/200
\end{aligned}
$$

Since

$$P(X \text{ or } Y \text{ or } Z) = P(X) + P(Y) + P(Z) - P(XY) - P(XZ)$$
$$- P(YZ) + P(XYZ)$$

then

$$P(X \text{ or } Y \text{ or } Z) = \frac{1}{8} + \frac{1}{10} + \frac{1}{25} - \frac{1}{25} - \frac{1}{50} - \frac{1}{100} + \frac{1}{200}$$

A common denominator of 200 will suit all fractions. Then

$$P(X \text{ or } Y \text{ or } Z) = \frac{25}{200} + \frac{20}{200} + \frac{8}{200} - \frac{8}{200} - \frac{4}{200} - \frac{2}{200} + \frac{1}{200}$$

$$= \frac{40}{200} = \frac{1}{5}$$

Therefore, the student may say that 1 American farm out of 5 grows either corn or wheat or rye.

Such problems arise in many fields. Their solutions are especially useful in a field called "market research." Many companies want to know certain characteristics of the American family. Questions in this field could be of the following types:

What is the probability that an American family has a washing machine or a dryer?

A mortgage on a house or a debt on a car? Many families have both.

A savings account or a checking account in a bank?

A TV set, a hi-fi set, or a tape recorder?

In a factory producing something that may have more than one defect, the question would be: What is the probability that our product has defect X; defect Y; defect Z; defect X, Y, or Z?

In any field, when one factor, X, contains elements of Y or Z, in any combinations, the formulas we have just learned may help solve a problem.

Multiplying probabilities

An ordinary deck of playing cards consists of 52 cards. They are divided into 4 main groups called *suits*. These are: clubs, diamonds, hearts, and spades. Within each suit there are 13 cards. These are: ace, king, queen, jack, and the numbers from 2 through 10. In many games the ace can be counted as the number 1 card. There are, therefore, 4 aces — one of each suit — and 4 of every other kind of card.

Suppose that you were asked: From a closed deck, what is the probability of drawing a spade? At this point, you know that the probability is 1/4, or 1 out of 4, since the deck is divided evenly into 4 suits.

Then, as a next step: What is the probability of drawing an ace? Since there are 4 aces in the deck of 52 cards, the probability is 4/52 or 1/13.

Joining the two events: What is the probability of drawing the ace of spades?

If you decided, on a hunch, to multiply the probability of spades by the probability of an ace, you would have

$$\frac{1}{4} \times \frac{1}{13} = \frac{1}{52}$$

And that would be right, as we know. Since there is only 1 ace of spades in the 52 cards, the probability of drawing it is 1 out of 52.

Speaking generally (about all cases and not just the one example), what has taken place? There has been the *simultaneous* (at the same time) success of two events.

PROBLEM: *What is the probability of getting 2 heads in 2 tosses of a coin?*

The probability on the first toss is 1/2, as we know. The probability on the second toss is also 1/2. Therefore, the probability of 2 heads in a row is $1/2 \times 1/2 = 1/4$.

We can prove that this is so by listing every possible combination of heads and tails that can occur when we toss a coin twice:

First	*Second*
toss	*toss*
head	*head*
head	*tail*
tail	*head*
tail	*tail*

Two heads on 2 tosses is only 1 of the 4 possible results.

Now we are ready to state the general rule to take care of all such situations.

Multiplication rule

If the first step can happen in 1 of X ways, and the second step can happen in 1 of Y ways, then both (together) can happen in XY ways (the product of X and Y).

Although the general rule is stated this way, it is not limited to only two probabilities. It is the *rule* no matter how many different steps are involved, as long as they are independent events.

PROBLEM 1: *What is the probability of getting:*

1. *Heads on a coin* and
2. *A 5 on a die* and
3. *The ace of spades from a deck of cards, one after the other?*

(*Note:* This is called a *compound event*. This merely means that it is a collection of *simple* events.)

Probability of

1. Heads $= 1/2$
2. 5 on a die $= 1/6$
3. Ace of spades $= 1/52$

Therefore, the probability of getting *all* of these is

$$\frac{1}{2} \times \frac{1}{6} \times \frac{1}{52} = \frac{1}{624}$$

We use the same rule whether the probability of success (P) or failure (Q) is involved.

PROBLEM 2: *A boy is playing a game in which 1 die is involved. An instruction card tells him what he must try to do. It says:*
   1. Come up with a 3 on the first throw.
   2. Come up with a 4 on the second throw.
   3. Come up with anything except a 5 on the third throw.

What is the probability that he will accomplish all this?

Probability of

1. A 3 on the first throw = 1/6
2. A 4 on the second throw = 1/6
3. Anything *except* 5 on the third throw = 5/6

(*Note:* Since anything *except* 5 means 1, 2, 3, 4, or 6, the probability is 5/6. He has 5 out of 6 possibilities of bringing this about.)

Therefore, the probability of accomplishing all 3 steps is

$$\frac{1}{6} \times \frac{1}{6} \times \frac{5}{6} = \frac{5}{216}$$

or about 1 chance out of 43.

From this example we can reach two conclusions:
   1. The rule holds no matter how many steps are involved.
   2. The rule holds even when there is a mixture of probabilities of success (P) and failure (Q).
   It is entirely possible to have a long chain of $P \times P \times Q \times Q \times P$, etc.

PROBLEM 3: *A girl has the following items of clothing in her wardrobe.*

5 blouses
3 skirts
3 scarves

Let's assume that they can all be mixed to make matching sets. (She likes blue and white so that she has blue polka dots, blue stripes, light blue, dark blue, and so on.)

How many days can she dress without having to wear the same outfit twice?

Probability of choosing a certain blouse: 1/5.

Probability of choosing a certain skirt: 1/3.

Probability of choosing a certain scarf: 1/3.

Therefore, the probability of the 3 in combination (the *simultaneous* happening of 3 events) is

$$\frac{1}{5} \times \frac{1}{3} \times \frac{1}{3} = \frac{1}{45}$$

She can go 45 days without wearing the same outfit twice.

PROBLEM 4 (Part 1): *Your parents take you to a restaurant. You study the menu. For your entree* (main course) *you have one choice from each of the following groups:*

> 1. *6 different meat dishes*
> 2. *5 different vegetables*
> 3. *3 kinds of potatoes*

Let's make one enormous assumption: You like all the choices equally well — even the vegetables! Now what's the probability of that?

Since you will select 1 from each group, how many different entrees can you make?

The probability of

> 1. Meat = 1/6
> 2. Vegetables = 1/5
> 3. Potatoes = 1/3

Therefore

$$\frac{1}{6} \times \frac{1}{5} \times \frac{1}{3} = \frac{1}{90}$$

The main course you finally select will be 1 out of 90 possible choices.

PROBLEM 4 (Part 2): *Your parents liked the restaurant so much that they return the following day. Lo and behold! The menu is exactly the same. You are determined to eat different foods today. How many different entrees can you choose from today?*

Each of the 3 groups has been reduced by 1. You now have a choice of:

1. 5 meat dishes $P = 1/5$
2. 4 vegetables $P = 1/4$
3. 2 potato dishes $P = 1/2$

Therefore

$$P = \frac{1}{5} \times \frac{1}{4} \times \frac{1}{2} = \frac{1}{40}$$

Since you now have only 40 possible entrees to choose from, you should be able to make up your mind much sooner.

PROBLEM 5: *A family living in New York City is planning a trip to Los Angeles and back. Both coming and going, they will stop in St. Louis, where the mother's family lives.*

In looking at maps, they find that there are 7 good routes from New York City to St. Louis and 5 from St. Louis to Los Angeles. In order to see more of the country, they decide not to follow the same routes in both directions.

In how many different ways can they make the trip?

Choice of routes:

Going: From New York City to St. Louis $P = 1/7$
           From St. Louis to Los Angeles $P = 1/5$

On the return trip, they have 1 choice less on each leg of the trip.

Return: From Los Angeles to St. Louis $P = 1/4$
            From St. Louis to New York City $P = 1/6$

Multiplying all probabilities:

$$\frac{1}{7} \times \frac{1}{5} \times \frac{1}{4} \times \frac{1}{6} = \frac{1}{840}$$

They have a choice of 840 different round trips.

You may have noticed that the travel problem and the restaurant problem have something in common. Both involve a "return trip" with each choice reduced by 1. However, the difference between them is more important than the similarity. In the travel problem, all 4 stages of the trip were being decided at once. They were "simultaneous," as was pointed out earlier.

If the family had said, "When we get to Los Angeles, we will decide what routes to follow on the way home," the problem would have been a different one.

In the restaurant problem, the boy's decisions were made on separate days. On his second visit, he might just as well have been in a different restaurant that offered 5 meat, 4 vegetable, and 2 potato dishes as choices.

This brings us to a very important point. In probability, the wording of a problem is often a key to the problem. One of the most beautiful examples of this is from Professor William Feller's book. In the three simple problems that follow, he shows how the wording of the problem affects the probability.

PROBLEM 1: In families with 2 children, *what is the probability of having* 2 boys?

The possibilities, in order of the oldest child first, are

> boy, boy
> boy, girl
> girl, boy
> girl, girl

In families with 2 children, the probability of having two boys is, therefore, 1 out of 4, or 1/4.

PROBLEM 2: *Granted that* a family has a boy. *What is the probability that* both *children are boys?*

The possibilities are

> boy, boy
> boy, girl
> girl, boy

The probability is, therefore, 1 out of 3, or 1/3.

(*Note:* We are talking about *both*, or a pair. Form a mental picture of where this information might come from. It might come from a file of family cards in the Town Hall. The cards we would choose to look at, or count, would be those having the 3 combinations shown above — a family having a boy.)

PROBLEM 3: We pick out a boy by chance. *It is learned that he comes from a family of 2 children. What is the probability that the* other *child is a boy?*

We are now talking *only about the other child*. The other child can only be a boy or a girl. The probability is, therefore, 1 out of 2, or 1/2, that the *other* child is a boy.

On many examinations, the first instruction is: READ THE PROBLEMS CAREFULLY. This is advice you should follow especially in solving probability problems.

Conditional probability

This is a term often used for situations not much different from the restaurant or travel problems. The problems are often worded this way: What is the probability that Y will take place once X has taken place?

This is the way the formula is usually written:

$$P(Y \text{ and } X) = P(X) \times P(Y/X)$$

$P(Y \text{ and } X)$ means the probability that Y and X will happen. $P(X)$ means the probability that X will happen. $P(Y/X)$ means the probability that Y will happen once X has happened.

Here is a typical problem.

PROBLEM: *Your father has to fix a chair. He needs 1-inch Philips screws (they are the ones with the cross $\oplus$ on top instead of a straight line $\ominus$). He keeps the 1-inch screws in a separate drawer of a cabinet. Since he bought them this week, he knows that there are 12 regular and 6 Philips screws.*

Without looking or feeling, he puts his hand into the drawer and picks out a Philips screw. Feeling lucky, he puts his hand in again and picks out another screw. What is the probability that this can be done twice?

At the start, there was a total of 18 screws. Six of these were of the Philips type. The probability on the first try was, therefore, 6 out of 18, or 6/18. This is our X value.

After he took out 1 Philips screw, there was a total of 17 screws left. Of these, 5 were now Philips screws. The probability of success on the second attempt was, therefore, 5 out of 17, or 5/17. This is our (Y/X). To word it technically, we say this is the probability that Y will happen once X has taken place. Since

$$P(Y \ and \ X) = P(X) \times P(Y/X)$$

then

$$P(Y \ and \ X) = \frac{6}{18} \times \frac{5}{17} = \frac{30}{306} = \frac{5}{51}$$

Having been successful the first time, your father has less than 1 out of 10 chances (5 out of 51) of being successful again.

Attacking a problem from the rear

The problems presented up to this point have ended with the question, "What is the probability of success?" Different words were used to suit each problem, but this is what was meant.

It is easier to solve some problems by asking instead, "What is the probability of failure?" — or, in other words, of *not* getting the thing we want.

All the probabilities of an event add up to 1, which stands for certainty. By subtracting the probability of failure from 1 (certainty), we obtain the probability of success.

The probability of getting "heads" on a coin (call this "success") is 1/2, as we know. This can be stated another way: The probability of getting "heads" = 1 — the probability of *not* getting heads, that is, of getting "tails."

P (of getting "heads") = 1 − 1/2 (the probability of tails)

PROBLEM (to be solved by the "minus probability" method): *Someone rolls three different dice. No two dice have the same number on top. What is the probability that one of the three dice has a 6 showing (comes up 6)?*

An important condition of the problem is that all 3 top faces have different numbers. Also, remember the *simultaneous* happenings. Therefore, probabilities are multiplied.

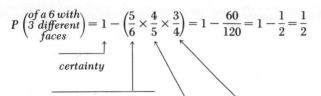

$$P \begin{pmatrix} of\ a\ 6\ with \\ 3\ different \\ faces \end{pmatrix} = 1 - \left(\frac{5}{6} \times \frac{4}{5} \times \frac{3}{4}\right) = 1 - \frac{60}{120} = 1 - \frac{1}{2} = \frac{1}{2}$$

certainty

there are 5 out of 6 ways of not getting 6

since no 2 faces are alike, there are now only 4 out of 5 ways of not getting 6

as in the last step, there are now only 3 out of 4 ways of not getting six

This method is not used "just to be different" or to show how clever we can be. Sometimes this *negative* approach helps to reason out a problem. But, most important, there are many problems that can be solved more simply this way.

One of the most fascinating and surprising problems in probability is solved by this method. We shall see it soon.

Buckets of probabilities

In hundreds of telephone exchanges, a record of the number of calls made and the number of "busy" signals is kept.

On an experimental farm of an agricultural college, the length of ears of corn is measured to see if a new seed has resulted in longer ears.

In a biological laboratory, cultures of bacteria in hundreds of special (Petri) dishes are carefully counted to see if a new drug has worked.

In one state, new traffic laws go into effect. Every car insurance company in the country keeps a special record of accidents in the state to see if the new laws have made a difference.

A product comes off a factory's machine in batches of ten. An inspector examines them, rejecting the bad ones. He keeps a record of the number of bad ones in each batch.

A new class of high-school graduates is taking college-entrance examinations. The mark of every student is carefully punched into an IBM card. How many will complete college? Can the marks tell us in advance?

A large department store opens 5,000 new charge accounts in a month. It keeps a careful record of how much each account will spend; also, of how many will turn out to be bad accounts.

A team of physicists in a space laboratory is measuring an important part of a new rocket. Each physicist on the team measures the part 25 times. All write down their results.

The above examples may be called "probability in action." The list could continue until the end of the book. In real life, probabilities are often the result of thousands and thousands of individual events.

After the information is collected, it is usually arranged as a frequency distribution of a type that we studied in an earlier chapter. The groups, or classes, of the frequency distribution would be arranged to suit the information. One type might be:

Length of ears of corn	*Number of ears of corn*
8 *and under* 8½ *inches*	50
8½ *and under* 9 *inches*	120
9 *and under* 9½ *inches*	215
etc.	*etc.*

Other information might be grouped according to "good" or "bad" characteristics:

Results of inspection of machine batches	*Number of batches*
0 *bad* (10 *good*)	15
1 *bad* (9 *good*)	40
2 *bad* (8 *good*)	95
etc.	*etc.*

Still other information might be grouped by exact numbers:

Number of busy signals *in one hour* *(on different switchboards)*	*Number of calls* *made*
0	1,000
1	2,500
2	5,000
etc.	etc.

Almost all probability distributions are of three major types. They include a wide range of human events. Other types of distributions are meant for very special cases. These major types are:

1. The normal distribution.
2. The binomial expansion.
3. The Poisson (Pwa-so') distribution.

It is beyond the scope of this book to present a technical discussion of these distributions. If you continue your studies, especially in *any* technical field, you are bound to meet them. You should, however, know what they are, how to recognize them, in what kind of situations they occur, what they measure, and how they can be used.

One thing must be said first. There is no sharp line of separation among them. They do not describe completely different worlds. Sometimes one flows into the other; sometimes one is a special case of another. But there are certainly situations where one of them *fits* much better than the other two.

The normal curve

At the 1964–1965 New York World's Fair, one of the most popular exhibits was that of IBM (International Business Machines Corporation). A feature of the exhibit was a "probability machine." This was a giant device (more than 14 feet high and 8 feet wide) that looked like a vertical pinball machine.

A cruder but somewhat similar machine was constructed by Sir Francis Galton (1822–1911), a famous English scientist and cousin of Charles Darwin. He called it a Quincunx, after a Roman coin that had five circles on it.

The Probability Machine was displayed at the IBM pavilion during the 1964–65 New York World's Fair. About 15,000 plastic balls dropped through a maze of wires to 21 chutes in about 15 minutes. As they fell, the balls tended to form a normal curve as shown on page 123. (IBM)

From the top center of the probability machine, a stream of 15,000 plastic balls poured down. On their way to the bottom, they passed through a maze of hundreds of aluminum pins. At the bottom, they fell into 21 different chutes. They were then raised to the top again in buckets.

The experiment lasted about fifteen minutes and was done again and again, day after day. Yet, on every trial, the 15,000 balls fell into the pockets (or chutes) in almost exactly the same way. They formed the design, or curve, shown below.

DRAWING OF ARRANGEMENT OF BALLS IN THE FORM OF A NORMAL CURVE ON IBM's PROBABILITY MACHINE

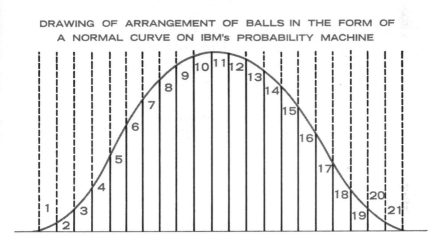

The probability of *any* ball landing in *any* pocket can be calculated from the type of fraction we have used before:

$$\frac{\text{the number of paths leading to the pocket}}{\text{the total number of paths}}$$

The curve that is formed by these 15,000 balls is called the *normal curve of probability.* Sometimes it is called the *Gaussian normal curve of error* after a famous German mathematician and astronomer, Karl Friedrich Gauss (1777–1855), who used it a great deal in his work. Because of its shape, it is often called the bell-shaped curve.

The word "normal" is used here in the sense of "usual." It doesn't mean that other curves are abnormal or freakish. Other patterns make other curves.

The normal curve is by far the most widely used of all probability curves. It would require several pages to list the different events that, in large numbers, follow the pattern of the normal curve. Practically all measurements follow the pattern — the lengths of ears of corn, the IQ's of all the students in a school, and so on. And it doesn't matter what you measure or how exact an instrument you use.

Examples:

A truck driver is backing a huge trailer truck into a parking space. He calls out to a passer-by, "Hey, buddy, how much room do I have?" "Three feet," the man answers. Being a scientist in disguise, the driver asks the next 5,000 people the same question and marks down the answers.

A policeman is chasing a thief. The thief, like a character from an old Charlie Chaplin comedy, runs across the Yankee Stadium playing field while a game is going on. He gets away while 15,000 people watch. To help identify the thief, the spectators are asked to write down how tall he was.

We're now in a large automobile factory. A machinist has made a small part for a car. It has to be accurate within 1/1,000th of an inch. (This is called the tolerance.) He measures it on a good caliper. A few thousand other machinists also measure it.

We are now at a laboratory of the Atomic Energy Commission. A particle's path is being measured on the world's finest electronic instrument. The measurements are within 1/1,000,000th of a centimeter. The measurement is made 5,000 times and an automatic record is kept.

All these measurements, rough or fine, have one thing in common. The *units* of measurement (feet, inches, or millionths of a centimeter) would be different. But if we made a graph of the frequency distribution of all the measurements, in each case they would all follow the normal curve.

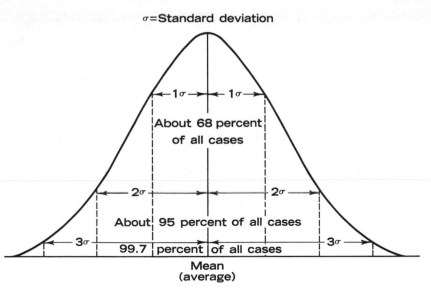

σ=Standard deviation

About 68 percent of all cases

About 95 percent of all cases

99.7 percent of all cases

Mean
(average)

At each end would be the few extreme (highest and low-est) measurements. At the center would be the mean (average) measurement. It would also be the measurement that was made most often. It is sometimes called the most probable measurement.

The kind of information that we can find in the normal curve can be seen from an example.

PROBLEM: *A university has given an entrance examination to high-school graduates. There were 150 questions, each worth 1 point. The papers are graded and the marks arranged in a frequency distribution.*

(*Note:* In the section on frequency distributions, a measure called the standard deviation was mentioned. It is shown by the Greek letter sigma, σ. In the Answer Section, the method of calculating sigma is shown on pages 253 and 254.)

Here is what we know about the examination after calculations:

> *The average (mean):*   *100*
> *The standard deviation*
>   (*sigma,* σ):   *20*

The dean of the school consults with his statistician. He says, "Next year we want to start an experimental program for students who score between 130 and 135 on the entrance exam. We expect the exam to be the same. About 2,000 students will take it. How many would be involved in the program?"

The statistician does not have to count marks. Since the exam will be about the same, he can find the answer for the dean from the mean and standard deviation—*because the information comes from a normal curve.*

Here is how he would solve the problem:

The dean is interested in the group scoring 130 to 135.

Step 1 (the differences from the mean)

135 − 100 (the mean) = 35
130 − 100 (the mean) = 30

Step 2 $\dfrac{\text{(the differences)}}{\text{(the standard deviation)}}$

$$\frac{\text{First difference}}{\text{Standard deviation}} = \frac{35}{20} = 1\tfrac{3}{4} \text{ standard deviations } (\sigma\text{'s})$$

$$\frac{\text{Second difference}}{\text{Standard deviation}} = \frac{30}{20} = 1\tfrac{1}{2} \text{ standard deviations } (\sigma\text{'s})$$

Step 3. The statistician would now look at one of the most important of all statistical tables. It is called "table of areas under the normal curve." There he will find what *percent* of the cases will fall *between the mean and 1¾ standard deviations, between the mean and 1½ standard deviations.* By subtracting one from the other, he will know what percent of students will achieve between 130 and 135 on the examination.

Let us assume that it is 3 percent (.03). This is an approximation. He now has to calculate 3 percent of 2,000 (the number expected to take the examination), and he can tell the dean what he wants to know.

2,000
× .03
─────
60.00

He tells the dean that about 60 students will score between 130 and 135.

If we know that our information follows a normal curve, we have a powerful tool for prediction. *Regardless of what the average (mean) is,* we know that

1 standard deviation on either side of the mean (+ or −) will include about 68 percent of our cases.

2 standard deviations on either side of the mean (+ or −) will include about 95 percent of our cases.

3 standard deviations on either side of the mean (+ or −) will include about 99.7 percent of our cases.

This accounts for all but 3 in 1,000.

The above, of course, does not include all the uses to which we can put the normal curve or all the information we can gain from it. Other uses, however, are far beyond the range of this book.

The binomial expansion

We now visit a cousin of the normal curve. Soon we shall see where the family lines meet.

There are two ways of recognizing a binomial distribution:

1. There are only 2 classes. These could be: heads, tails; good, bad; success, failure; boy, girl; in, out; fair, foul. There's really no limit.

2. The events are *independent* events. The probabilities remain the same from trial to trial.

Although there are two classes, the probabilities do not have to be 1/2 and 1/2, as they are with heads and tails or boys and girls. Fair and foul balls in relation to baseball may have probabilities of 9/10 and 1/10; in relation to weather, fair and foul may have probabilities of 4/5 and 1/5.

Those who have studied elementary algebra will be familiar with the binomial expansion.

Suppose we have $(X + Y)^2$. We can expand this [multiply $(X + Y)$ by itself the necessary number of times] by simple multiplication.

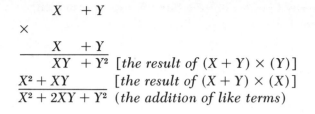

To expand $(X + Y)^3$, we can multiply $(X^2 + 2XY + Y^2) \times (X + Y)$. But as the power (exponent) becomes higher and higher, this becomes more and more tiring.

Fortunately, two very simple tools can be used to help solve any expansion.

1. The X's and Y's follow a definite, simple order. For example, let's expand $(X + Y)^4$.

The terms of the expansion are

$$X^4 + X^3Y^{(1)} + X^2Y^2 + X^{(1)}Y^3 + Y^4$$

You can see that the exponent of X keeps going down by 1; the exponent of Y keeps going up by 1. [The 1's in parentheses (1) are usually not shown.]

The only thing we need to complete the expansion is the *number* of X^4, the number of X^3Y, etc. These are called the *coefficients*.

2. To find the coefficients, we have one of the most beautiful tools in mathematics. It is called *Pascal's triangle*, shown on page 129. It was developed by Blaise Pascal (1623–1662), a Frenchman, one of the greatest mathematical geniuses who ever lived. He is called by many the father of probability theory.

By merely reading the numerals in the triangle, we can find the coefficients for any expansion.

We are expanding $(X + Y)^4$; therefore, follow the diagonal arrow to 4. In that *row* you will find the coefficients of our different X,Y combinations. We now write the entire expansion:

$$(X + Y)^4 = (1)X^4 + 4X^3Y^1 + 6X^2Y^2 + 4X^1Y^3 + (1)Y^4$$

or, as it would usually be written:

$$(X + Y)^4 = X^4 + 4X^3Y + 6X^2Y^2 + 4XY^3 + Y^4$$

One of the beauties of Pascal's triangle is that you can easily make it up yourself. Every coefficient is the sum of the two coefficients above it in the columns to the left and right, as shown in the encircled numbers.

PASCAL'S TRIANGLE OF BINOMIAL COEFFICIENTS
Up to the power 10. Example: $(X+Y)^{10}$

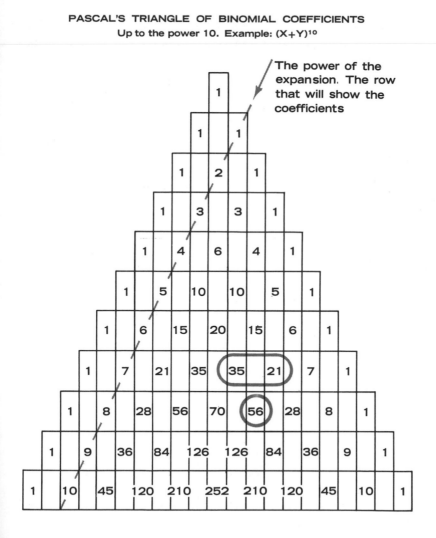

The power of the expansion. The row that will show the coefficients

Uses of the binomial expansion

Let's get back on the main track to see how the binomial expansion works in probability theory.

PROBLEM 1: *I toss 2 coins. How many different combinations of heads and tails will there be? How many of each combination?*

Using the binomial expansion, I can write it this way:

$$(H + T)^2 = (1)H^2 + 2H^1T^1 + (1)T^2$$

where the exponent of $(H + T)$, 2 in this case, is equal to the number of coins tossed.

This expansion tells me that I can have:

the coefficients $\begin{cases} 1 \text{ combination of 2 heads} \\ 2 \text{ combinations of 1 head and 1 tail} \\ 1 \text{ combination of 2 tails} \end{cases}$ *the exponents*

PROBLEM 2: *In families of 6 children, what are likely to be the boy-girl combinations? What is the probability of having 3 boys and 3 girls?*

$$(B + G)^6 = (1)B^6 + 6B^5G^1 + 15B^4G^2 + 20B^3G^3 + 15B^2G^4$$
$$+ 6B^1G^5 + (1)G^6$$

This distribution of boys and girls in families with 6 children is likely to be:

1 family with: 6 boys, 0 girls (B^6)
6 families with: 5 boys, 1 girl $(6B^5G)$
15 families with: 4 boys, 2 girls $(15B^4G^2)$
20 families with: 3 boys, 3 girls $(20B^3G^3)$
15 families with: 2 boys, 4 girls $(15B^2G^4)$
6 families with: 1 boy, 5 girls $(6BG^5)$
1 family with: 0 boys, 6 girls (G^6)
64 (the sum of the coefficients)

Since there are 64 families in all and 20 with an even number of boys and girls, the probability of having 3 boys and 3 girls is 20/64 = 5/16.

What happens when the probabilities of the two classes are not even, as they are with head and tail, boy and girl? The method used is exactly the same.

PROBLEM 3: *A chicken farm classifies its eggs by large and small. After thousands of sorting tests, it has found that of 10 eggs, 7 will be large, 3 small.*
In 4 eggs, what is likely to be the mixture of large and small?

Large (L): probability $= 7/10$, or .7
Small (S): probability $= 3/10$, or .3

We find, by use of the binomial expansion, that

$$(L + S)^4 = L^4 + 4L^3S + 6L^2S^2 + 4LS^3 + S^4$$

(*Reminder:* When the exponent is 1, we need not write it.)
To find the proportions, substitute .7 for L and .3 for S. Then

$$(L + S)^4 = (.7)^4 + 4(.7)^3(.3) + 6(.7)^2(.3)^2 + 4(.7)(.3)^3 + (.3)^4$$

After the multiplications are completed, this is the result:

Probability of:

4 large eggs:	.240 or	24.0	percent
3 large, 1 small:	.411 or	41.1	percent (rounded)
2 large, 2 small:	.265 or	26.5	percent
1 large, 3 small:	.076 or	7.6	percent
4 small eggs:	.008 or	0.8	percent
Sum of all probabilities:	1.000 or	100.0	percent

The sum of the probabilities is 1, exactly what it should be.

We said earlier that the binomial expansion and the normal curve are related. As the number of trials, tests, experiments, or events is increased and the results are plotted on a graph, the curve of the binomial expansion takes the shape of the normal curve.

For example, each of 1,000 people tosses 10 coins. We make a record of the results and then plot them on a graph. The graph will show how many of the 1,000 had ten heads, how many had 9 heads and 1 tail, and so on. The graph of the results will most likely form a normal curve. From such distributions, the calculations of the mean and the standard deviation are extremely simple:

$$\text{Average (mean)}\,(\bar{x}) = N \times P$$

the number   the probability
of trials   of success in
                     one trial

$$\text{Standard deviation}\,(\sigma) = \sqrt{NPQ}$$

which means the square root ($\sqrt{}$) of the number of trials (N) times the probability of success (P) times the probability of failure (Q).

PROBLEM 4: *Seven hundred and twenty people throw a die. What will be the probable number of 5's? What will be the standard deviation?*

$P(5) = 1/6 \qquad Q(5) = 5/6 \qquad N = 720$

$\text{Mean} = N \times P = 720 \times 1/6 = 120$

$\text{Standard deviation} = \sqrt{NPQ} = \sqrt{720 \times 1/6 \times 5/6}$

$$= \sqrt{\frac{3{,}600}{36}} = \sqrt{100} = 10$$

Using what we know about the relationship between the mean and the standard deviation, we can make a broader statement about the average number of 5's on 720 tosses.

$\text{Mean} + 3 \text{ standard deviations} = 120 + 30 = 150$
$\text{Mean} - 3 \text{ standard deviations} = 120 - 30 = 90$

Therefore, there are 997 chances out of 1,000 that in 720 tosses the number of 5's that turn up will be between 90 and 150. You should know, at this point, that the importance of this tool is not in knowing how a die will fall. Can you think of some serious applications?

There are, of course, standard tables of values for the binomial distribution. Through the use of computers, these tables have recently been expanded.

The Poisson distribution

The lives of great scientists or mathematicians are seldom the subject of movies. They are considered to be not as exciting as those of kings, generals, or athletes. I cannot recall a single movie about Sir Isaac Newton, but in how many has Napoleon appeared? Would anyone care to argue which man had the more lasting effect on human affairs?

Naturally, great mathematicians and scientists do things that most other people do. As children, they play youthful pranks and their parents probably worry about what will become of them. When they are young, they study, begin to do their work, fall in love, marry, and have children.

The high point in their life usually comes when they write a scientific paper or book or deliver a talk before a body of other scientists or mathematicians. Slowly, the world may begin to realize that they are exceptional men.

In rare cases, something is associated with their name, like Halley's comet, Pascal's triangle, the Poisson distribution, or the Van Allen radiation belt. But that is not enough for a movie.

Until a movie can be made to show, in an interesting way, the workings of the brain — how an idea is born, how it develops, how it clicks into final form — scientists and mathematicians will not be considered interesting subjects for movies. We will have to learn to make the birth of an idea as interesting and exciting as a punch thrown by a heavyweight champion.

Siméon Denis Poisson (1781–1840) was a famous French physicist and mathematician. His parents wanted him to study law. He failed at that. They wanted him, then, to become a surgeon. He failed at that, too. They began to think that he would never amount to anything. Then he discovered that his real interest was in mathematics and science. At twenty-five, he was a full professor at the Ecole Polytechnique, France's highest engineering college. After that, for many years, he was on the faculty of science of the University of Paris. His main field of interest was the application of mathematics to physics. During his lifetime, he wrote more than three hundred scientific papers and several books. They were in the fields of astronomy, physics, and mathematics. Some of his physics books were standard textbooks until the rapid advance of technical knowledge made them out of date.

In 1837, Poisson wrote a book that, in English, may be called *Research into Probabilities in Civil and Criminal Court Decisions*. This may seem like a very strange application of probability theory. But even Laplace, the great eighteenth-century French genius who contributed so many important ideas to mathematics and astronomy, as well as to the theory of probability, was interested in this field. Unlike Poisson's books on physics, this book presented ideas that grew and grew. In recent years greater and greater use has been found for Poisson's formulas and distributions.

You may get some idea of how far the uses have advanced from this amusing example. In many old books on probability, one classical example of the Poisson distribution was almost always included. It has to do with the number of German army troopers killed in each corps from 1875 to 1894 as a result of being kicked by a cavalry horse!

The Poisson distribution is used under these conditions:

1. When *the number of cases (n)*, trials, experiments, tests, etc., is *very large.*

2. When *the probability (p)* on one trial is *extremely small.*

3. When there is *a set of definite but moderate* values that X, the unknown value, can reach. (The values may be 0, 1, 4, 7, etc.)

Because n is so large and p so small, they are usually written together as a unit—np. Then a new letter is substituted to stand for the combination. Most often, $np = m$. Whenever you see m in a Poisson formula, it is intended to stand for np.

A very unusual thing about the Poisson distribution is that

It is not necessary to know the value of n; we only need to know that it is large.

Here is an example of how it can be used.

As you may know, misprints in books are rare. Suppose that it is found that there are 2 misprints in every 100 printed pages. A misprint may be only one letter. Think of the thousands of letters on 100 pages of a book! We know, therefore, that n (the number of letters) is large. We don't have to count them. In this case we can say:

$np = m = 2$ (the probable number of misprints in 100 pages)

The formula for a Poisson distribution is somewhat complicated. Discussion of it is beyond the range of this book. But because you may meet it some day, it is shown in the Answer Section with one simple problem worked out.

Where does the Poisson distribution meet the two distributions discussed earlier (the normal and binomial)? In certain cases, the results obtained by the Poisson method are very close to those that arise from using the binomial expansion.

Today, the Poisson distribution is used in many fields. The case of misprints in books has been mentioned. It can also be used to estimate the number of raisins in raisin bread. Professor Feller, in his book, cites some rather more important uses.

These are examples of situations where a Poisson distribution is used:

1. Radioactive disintegration of certain atomic particles.
2. Flying-bomb hits on areas of London during World War II.
3. The interchange of chromosomes in cells.
4. Wrong-number connections in telephone exchanges.
5. Bacteria counts and blood counts in Petri dishes in biology experiments.

Recently, this writer had an interesting experience. In *The New York Times* of August 5, 1964, there was a report of an experiment performed at the Brookhaven National Laboratory where many experiments of the Atomic Energy Commission are carried out. This laboratory has one of the world's largest atom-smashers.

The experiment was a very technical one, having to do with the nature of sub-atomic particles (the particles that make up the atom). One of these is known as a meson. This is supposed to be the "glue" that holds the particles together. In the body of the report was this paragraph: "Now evidence of the existence of this decay mode has been obtained through identification of the forbidden particles as the end products of 2 of each 1,000 decays in which K-2 mesons participate."

The "forbidden particles" were thought not to exist in such situations. My first reaction was, "A perfect set-up for a Poisson distribution."

The article did not say whether such an analysis was made. My guess is that it either was or will be made.

But the point is the thrill of recognition. It is to be hoped that you, too, will enjoy the thrill of recognition when you happen to come across material that your new-found knowledge will help you to understand.

More probability?

The modern computer is introducing probability into new fields. It is also creating new fields of probability. We would like to end this section with an example that you may find interesting and amusing.

There are many fields in which the collection of information from which to estimate probabilities is impossible. The trials or experiments may be too costly. They may take too long a time or be very rare events. They may also be so complicated that, under ordinary conditions, the time and effort of very many people would be required to calculate the probabilities.

In such cases, sets of conditions are "imagined"; they are made up. Then they are placed in a computer with the proper sets of controls on the experiment. The computer is "told" what to do. After a few minutes, it presents distributions. From these, probabilities are calculated.

The entire operation is like a game. And do you know its name? It is called Monte Carlo, after the most famous gambling casino in the world! Evidently, probabilists cannot separate themselves from gambling.

Coins, dice, playing cards, roulette—these are important tools for testing or broadening probability theory, and as we have said before, they make such perfect models that probabilists cannot help playing with them.

The relationship between gambling and probability theory was best expressed by Karl Pearson (1857–1936), a British scientist who made many contributions to statistical theory. A quotation of his cited by Dr. Warren Weaver in his fine book, *Lady Luck*, may serve to justify this relationship. Pearson said, "The record of a month's roulette playing at Monte Carlo can afford us material for discussing the foundations of knowledge."

A grab bag of probability

If you have ever been to a party at which a grab bag has been part of the entertainment, you know how much fun it can be. Each guest brings an unmarked gift that is meant to be humorous. The gifts are placed in a basket, and at some point during the party, each guest picks one. Very often the picking is done blindfolded.

The humor is in the cleverness of the gifts or in their unsuitability. A boy often gets a gift more suitable for a girl. A high-school girl may receive an ABC book.

This grab bag is organized along the same lines. You may ask: Why compare problems with "gifts"? The answer is simple. Most people enjoy puzzles. There are plenty of challenging puzzles here.

As in a grab bag, many of the problems won't "suit" you. Some are more difficult than the ones that were presented earlier, but you should find them entertaining reading, in any case. Included here are some of the most famous problems in probability.

Since this chapter does represent a serious attempt to explain the fundamentals of probability, the grab bag has a serious purpose. Some problems combine elements discussed in separate places. Others introduce new elements that are too difficult for this beginner's chapter on probability. However, by means of interesting problems, you may get some idea of the wide range of problems that probability theory deals with.

But, above all, the purpose of this section is to amuse and entertain. This is an invitation to you to join in the fun.

PROBLEM 1: *Lateness in school is an important problem. Let us solve one problem having to do with lateness.*

A boy is late 6 times in as many weeks. This worries his teacher. In examining her records, she finds that all his latenesses were on Wednesdays.

What is the probability that this is just a coincidence?

There are 5 school days. The probability that a lateness will fall on Wednesday, by chance, is 1 out of 5, or 1/5th. As it fell on the same day 6 times, the probability of a coincidence is

$$\left(\frac{1}{5}\right)^6 = \frac{1}{15,625}$$

Since it is not likely that the latenesses all fell on Wednesdays by chance, the teacher talks to the boy to find out what the reason is.

PROBLEM 2: *A common type of problem in probability is called "fitting balls into cells." It takes many forms. We saw it in the "cookies in the jars" problem.*

When the number of balls and cells is the same, there is a simple formula for finding the probability of filling all the cells if the balls are put in by chance.

Letting x = the number of balls and cells, the formula is

$$P = \frac{X!}{X^x}$$

In a class, 5 students are absent each week. What is the probability that 1 will be out on each school day? Here, we are pairing students and days as we do balls and cells.

$$P = \frac{5!}{5^5} = \frac{120}{3,125} = \frac{24}{625}$$

This means that in 625 weeks, there will be only 24 weeks when 1 student is out each day. This reduces to about 1 week in 26 when 1 student is out each day. In all other weeks, there will be days when 2 or 3 or more students are out. In other words, although 5 students will be out during the week, there will be days with 100 percent attendance.

PROBLEM 3: *In mid-season, a baseball roster often includes the following players:*

> *8 pitchers*
> *3 catchers*
> *8 infielders*
> *6 outfielders*

As you may know, on the playing field there are

> *1 pitcher*
> *1 catcher*
> *4 infielders*
> *3 outfielders*

We will assume that the team is the New York Mets of 1964, so that it doesn't really matter what infield position an infielder plays. The same is true for the outfield. How many different starting line-ups can be made?

1. A pitcher can be chosen in 1 out of 8 ways. $P = 1/8$.

2. A catcher can be chosen in 1 out of 3 ways. $P = 1/3$.

3. How many combinations can be made of 8 infielders, taken 4 at a time?

$$8 \ C \ 4 = \frac{8!}{4! \ (8-4)!} = \frac{8!}{4! \times 4!} = \frac{8 \times 7 \times 6 \times 5}{24} = \frac{1,680}{24} = 70$$

$P = 1/70$ (for infield combination)

4. How many combinations can be made of 6 outfielders taken 3 at a time?

$$6 \ C \ 3 = \frac{6!}{3! \ (6-3)!} = \frac{6!}{3! \times 3!} = \frac{6 \times 5 \times 4}{6} = \frac{120}{6} = 20$$

$P = 1/20$ (for outfield combination)

5. Since all play on the field simultaneously (we hope), the probabilities must be multiplied:

$$P = \frac{1}{8} \times \frac{1}{3} \times \frac{1}{70} \times \frac{1}{20} = 33,600$$

It may seem startling that from 33,600 possible line-ups, the New York Mets have not found a winning line-up yet.

PROBLEM 4: *You have probably been in a group that had to pick folded slips of paper for a prize, with one slip a winner. Does it make any difference in your chances of winning if you get first pick, second pick, or last pick?*

There are 5 closed slips. One of them is a winner. Five people will each have a chance to pick. You are second. Do you have as much chance as the first picker?

The first person's chances are, of course, 1 out of 5, or 1/5.

As you wait your turn, you say to yourself, "If he picks the winner, the whole thing is over. If he doesn't, my chances will be one out of 4." Therefore, your chance is a combination of his *failure* to pick a winner (4/5) times the probability of your success (1/4). Therefore, $4/5 \times 1/4 = 1/5$—exactly the same as his.

For the third person, it is, $4/5 \times 3/4 \times 1/3 = 1/5$, also.

PROBLEM 5: *Those who are familiar with the game of poker should find this problem interesting.*

Most poker players would like to see a pair or 3 of a kind, or something as good, when they look at their cards after they are dealt. Most often, though, they see 5 different face cards. Is luck against them?

What is the probability of drawing 5 different face cards? (They could make a straight. But the probability of that is small—only about 1/300.)

All possible 5-card poker hands in a deck of 52 cards are

52 *C* 5 = 2,598,960

1. The 5 different cards can be chosen in 13 *C* 5 ways.

2. With each card there is 1 out of 4 suits to choose from. Therefore, the probability of 5 different face cards is

$$\frac{(4)^5 \times 13 \ C \ 5}{2,598,960} = \frac{1,317,888}{2,598,960} = \text{approximately } \frac{51}{100}$$

In other words, the chances are a little better than even (½) that a player will draw 5 different face cards when the game starts. So luck is not against him.

Incidentally, if your parents play bridge (in bridge, each of the 4 players is dealt 13 cards), you can tell them that the number of possible hands is

52 *C* 13 = 635,013,559,600

(Yes, that's *billions*.)

PROBLEM 6: *The Delightful Dairy Company sells chocolate milk and skim milk as well as regular milk. The chocolate and skim milk are in green containers. Regular milk comes in a red container.*

1. Of 100 containers, 6 are filled with chocolate milk.

2. Of 5,000 containers, 25 are filled with skim milk.

A shopper in the retail department absent-mindedly picks up a green container. What is the probability that it is chocolate milk?

There are at least two ways of solving this problem.

Method A. Since skim milk is 25 out of 5,000, change the ratio of chocolate milk to a basis of 5,000. Six out of 100 is the same as 300 out of 5,000. (Five thousand is 50 times as much as 100. Therefore, multiply the 6 by 50, also: 50 × 6 = 300.) Now we know:

1. Of 5,000 containers, 300 are filled with chocolate milk.

2. Of 5,000 containers, 25 are filled with skim milk.

The probability that the container is filled with chocolate milk is:

$$\frac{300 \text{ chocolate milk}}{325 \text{ all milk in green containers}} = \frac{12}{13}$$

The probability is 12/13 that the container picked by chance is filled with chocolate milk.

Method B. If you have no difficulty in working with percents, this method is simple.

1. Chocolate milk: 6 out of 100 = 6.0 percent.

$$\frac{6}{100} \times 100 = 6.0$$

2. Skim milk: 25 out of 5,000 = 0.5 percent.

$$\frac{25}{5,000} \times 100 = 0.5$$

Since 6.0 percent is 12 times as large as 0.5 percent, there are 12 units of chocolate milk to 1 unit of skim milk. The total is 13 units, of which 12 are chocolate milk.

Don't be fooled by a mixture of large and small numbers.

PROBLEM 7: Don't try to solve this problem at first reading. Read it and enjoy it. If you understand the principle involved, you may learn to use it.

When you were younger, you may have played a card game called War. If you have younger brothers or sisters, this may be true today.

In this game, the two players use either two full decks of regular playing cards or one deck, equally divided. The decks are kept face down and each player opens 1 card at a time. The cards are matched, and high card wins. If the 2 cards match exactly (king and king, for example), the players shout War. There is then a play-off, usually a 5-card run, to see who wins.

For the purposes of this problem, we assume that the decks, of any size, are equally paired; that is, each player has the same number of aces, kings, etc.

Those who know the game may be surprised to learn that it is an old French and English game known as Rencontre or Coincidence.

The basic problem of how many wars to expect was solved by the mathematician Montmort in 1708. Not surprisingly, in probability books it is called Montmort's problem.

In two 5-card decks, with matching cards, what is the probability of having no wars (or matches)?

$$P(\text{no wars}) = \frac{1}{2!} - \frac{1}{3!} + \frac{1}{4!} - \frac{1}{5!} = \frac{1}{2} - \frac{1}{6} + \frac{1}{24} - \frac{1}{120}$$

(change to a common denominator)

$$= \frac{60}{120} - \frac{20}{120} + \frac{5}{120} - \frac{1}{120} = \frac{44}{120} = \frac{11}{30}$$

The probability of having no wars in 5 cards is a little better than 1 out of 3.

b. In 5 cards, what is the probability of having exactly *1 war?*

$$P(1 \text{ war}) = 1 - \frac{1}{2!} + \frac{1}{3!} - \frac{1}{4!} + \frac{1}{5!} = 1 - \frac{44}{120} = \frac{76}{120} = \frac{19}{30}$$

The probability of having exactly 1 war in 5 cards is almost 2 out of 3.

Now here is an amazing thing. The probability of exactly 1 war in 4 cards, 5 cards, 6 cards — up to any number of cards, including a deck of 52, changes very, very little. It remains at about 2 chances out of 3.

Look at the factorial numbers in the denominator. They keep rising. The fractions that we keep adding and subtracting become so small so quickly that they hardly affect the probability. For example, the next fraction would be: $\frac{-1}{6!} = \frac{-1}{720}$. The following one would be: $\frac{+1}{7!} = \frac{+1}{5,040}$. The probability is barely affected.

c. What is the probability of exactly 5 *wars in a full deck of 52 cards?*

$$\frac{1}{5!} \left(1 - \frac{1}{1!} + \frac{1}{2!} - \frac{1}{3!} + \frac{1}{4!} - \frac{1}{5!} + \frac{1}{6!} + \cdots + \frac{1}{52!} \right)$$

The answer is about 1 in 300 (1/300).

d. Here is a problem you may now be able to solve by following the steps as above.
You have been invited to a party. As part of the entertainment

there will be a grab bag. Every guest brings a wrapped present with no identification on it. They are placed in a basket, and everyone picks a gift without looking at them (by chance). There are 8 guests present.
What is the probability that no one will pick his own gift?
Isn't this really the same as no wars in 8 cards?

$$\frac{1}{2!} - \frac{1}{3!} + \frac{1}{4!} - \frac{1}{5!} + \frac{1}{6!} - \frac{1}{7!} + \frac{1}{8!}$$

$$= \frac{1}{2} - \frac{1}{6} + \frac{1}{24} - \frac{1}{120} + \frac{1}{720} - \frac{1}{5,040} + \frac{1}{40,320}$$

(The last term can always be made the common denominator.)

$$\frac{20,160 - 6,720 + 1,680 - 336 + 56 - 8 + 1}{40,320} = \frac{14,833}{40,320}$$

Again, the probability (as in "no wars in 5 cards") is a little better than 1 out of 3. You see that the extra factorial terms made almost no difference.

PROBLEM 8 (let's relax with an easy one): *You toss a coin until the same side comes up twice in a row (head, head or tail, tail).*

What is the probability that an even *number of tosses will be needed?*

Possible results in 2 tosses	*Possible results in 3 tosses*	
H H — winner	H H H ⎱	game would have ended on
T T — winner	H H T ⎰	2nd toss
H T	H T T — winner	
T H	H T H	
	T T T ⎱	game would have ended on
	T T H ⎰	2nd toss
	T H H — winner	
	T H T	

With 2 tosses, the winning possibilities are 2 out of 4 = 1/2
With 3 tosses, the winning possibilities are 2 out of 8 = 1/4
Total possibilities = 3/4

The ratio of these probabilities then is 2 : 1 (1/2 to 1/4).
The probability of winning on an even number of tosses is

$\dfrac{1/2}{3/4}$ (This is a compound fraction which may be easily reduced to a simple one by multiplying both the numerator and denominator by the reciprocal of the denominator.)

$$\frac{1/2}{3/4} = \frac{1/2 \times 4/3}{3/4 \times 4/3} = \frac{1/2 \times 4/3}{1} = \frac{4}{6} \text{ or } \frac{2}{3}$$

Therefore, the probability of winning on an even number of tosses is 2/3, or 2 out of 3.

(*Note:* It can be shown that the same ratio exists between 4 and 5 tosses, 6 and 7 tosses, and so on.)

PROBLEM 9: A very interesting and important problem in probability is the question of *changes in lead*. The changes in lead may have to do with coin-tossing, the counting of ballots in an election, almost anything with a steady stream of events. The details of solving problems of *lead* are far too technical for this book. Remember that this book is a beginning in probability. We are very far from the end of the subject.

Some of the conditions of changes in lead may surprise you. In coin-tossing, *the most probable* number of changes in lead is zero. In other words, it is more likely that the person who is ahead after several tosses will stay ahead than that he will be overtaken. It follows that 1 change in lead is more probable than 2; 2 more probable than 3; and so on.

Even the number of ties (tie scores) is small in relation to the number of tosses. It does not follow that the number of ties will increase directly with the number of tosses. In 100,000 tosses of a coin, there are likely to be only *10* times as many ties as in 1,000 tosses.

Despite the complicated nature of the problem of leads, there is one very simple formula by which we can estimate the probability that a lead changes.

Consider this problem: In your school there has been an election for class president. Candidate X received 250 votes. Candidate Y received 150 votes. During the counting, what is the probability that the lead changed from X to Y and back?

The formula that is used is

$$P = \frac{X - Y}{X + Y}$$ X = the final, total vote for candidate X
  Y = the final, total vote for candidate Y

$$\frac{X - Y}{X + Y} = \frac{250 - 150}{250 + 150} = \frac{100}{400} = \frac{1}{4}$$

The probability is 1 out of 4 (1/4) that X was always in the lead.

If candidate X had received the same vote (250) but candidate Y had received only 50 votes, the probability would be 2 out of 3 that X would always have been in the lead during the counting of the votes.

As we would expect, the more one-sided the victory (or score), the more likely it is, that the winner always is in the lead.

PROBLEM 10: *The probability of getting 2 aces (or 1's) on 2 throws of a die is 1/6 × 1/6 = 1/36. How much better are your chances of getting 2 aces (or 1's) on 4 throws of a die?*

$$4 \, C \, 2 \times (1/6)^2 \times (5/6)^2$$

| the number of combinations of 4 dice in sets of 2 | the probability of a 1 twice | the probability of "not a 1" twice; 2 throws must not be a 1 |

$$P = \frac{4!}{2! \, 2!} \times \frac{1}{36} \times \frac{25}{36} = \frac{4 \times 3 \times 1 \times 25}{2 \times 36 \times 36} = \frac{300}{2592} = \frac{25}{216}$$

You now have about 1 chance out of 9. The probability of getting exactly 2 aces in 4 throws of a die is 25/216.

PROBLEM 11: *You toss 3 coins; your friend tosses 2 coins. What is the probability that you will toss more heads than he will?*

Look at the table on page 147. Your tosses include 12 possible heads; his include 4 heads. Altogether, there are 12 + 4, or 16, possible heads. Of these, 12 are yours so that your probability of tossing more heads is 12/16 = 3/4. Since 4 of the total of 16 heads will be your friend's, his probability of tossing more heads is only 4/16 = 1/4.

| Your probabilities: The number of ways your coins can fall | | | His probabilities: The number of ways his coins can fall | |
Coin 1	Coin 2	Coin 3	Coin 1	Coin 2
H	H	H	H	H
H	T	H	H	T
H	T	T	T	H
H	H	T	T	T
T	T	T		
T	H	T		
T	T	H		
T	H	H		

With only 1 coin more (50 percent more coins than he has, 3 against 2) your chances of winning are 3 times as good as his, 3/4 to 1/4.

PROBLEM 12: *We come now to one of the most famous problems in probability. Some day, if you study probability, you will find it in almost every book. It is called the birthday problem.*

The heart of the problem is this: How many people are needed altogether (in a classroom, for example) so that there is an even chance (1/2) of finding at least 2 people with the same birthday?

The answer will surprise you considering that there are 365 days in the year. It is only 23.

You will probably find this hard to believe until you have tested it several times. You may want to ask your teacher to make the test in your class.

Do not try to work this out. The numbers become extremely large very quickly. In mathematics, there are ways of handling such large numbers in simple fashion.

The method of solution is shown here.

First of all, we assume a year of 365 days.

The solution is of the *negative type* discussed elsewhere. We ask ourselves: What is the probability that the second person *does not* have the same birthday as the first; that the third person *does not* have the same birthday as either the first or second; and so on.

In a sense, this is what we are doing:

$$P = \left(1 - \frac{1}{365}\right) \times \left(1 - \frac{2}{365}\right) \times \left(1 - \frac{3}{365}\right) \times \cdots$$

This can be simplified. For example, this is the way the formula looks for the probability that among 10 people no 2 have the same birthday.

$$\frac{365}{365} \times \frac{364}{365} \times \frac{363}{365} \times \frac{362}{365} \times \frac{361}{365} \times \frac{360}{365} \times \frac{359}{365} \times \frac{358}{365} \times \frac{357}{365} \times \frac{356}{365}$$

The result is that, among 10 people, the chances are about 88 out of 100 that *no 2 people have the same birthday.* Therefore, the probability is about 12 out of 100 that at least 2 people *do* have the same birthday. This, in itself, is surprising—that among 10 people, the chances are better than 3/25 (12 out of 100) that at least 2 people have the same birthday.

If the multiplications are continued for 23 people, we find the chances to be almost 51 out of 100 (slightly better than 1/2) that at least 2 people have the same birthday.

Of course, if there are more than 23 people in a group, the chances improve. With 30 people, the chances are almost 7 out of 10 that at least two people will have the same birthday.

PROBLEM 13: *Let's relax now by doing some less complicated negative thinking. This time we will use cards instead of calendars.*

You know that a deck of playing cards has 4 equal suits: clubs, diamonds, hearts, and spades. If you were given 4 separate picks, you would expect to pick a spade at least once, wouldn't you? The probability on each pick is, of course, 1/4, if you replace the card in the deck after the pick.

What is the probability, under these conditions, that you will pick a spade once *in 4 picks?*

We use the *negative* approach by asking: What is the probability of *not* picking a spade?

The formula to use is

$$P = 1 - \left(\frac{3}{4}\right)^4 \leftarrow \textit{the number of picks}$$

certainty   *the probability of* not
getting a spade

After completing the multiplications we have

$$1 - \frac{81}{256} = \frac{175}{256}$$

This is about 68 chances out of 100.

If you are given 5 picks: $P = 1 - (3/4)^5$, so the chances rise to about 76 out of 100.

Here is how your chances improve with the number of picks:

Number of picks	Probability	Increase in probability in 100 picks
4	About 68 out of 100	
5	About 76 out of 100	8
6	About 82 out of 100	6
7	About 87 out of 100	5
8	About 90 out of 100	3

You can see that the *increase* in the probability (last column) grows smaller and smaller.

You can never, no matter how many picks you are given, reach absolute certainty. You will come very close. But can there be any assurance, if you replace the card you pick, that you will definitely pick a spade?

Certainty is a probability of 1; in this case, 100 out of 100.

Can you see, by logical reasoning, why you come closer and closer to certainty without ever really reaching it?

PROBLEM 14: *This problem is a little more complicated than the milk problem, but the idea behind it is the same.*

At Certain City Stadium, there are 3 turnstiles, marked A, B, and C. Some of the customers who go through them have paid for tickets; others have entered with free passes. A study of the ticket stubs has shown how many people use the different turnstiles and what percent come in on passes at each one.

Here are the results:

Turnstile	Percent of people who use it	Percent of tickets at each turnstile that are free passes
A	20.0	5.0
B	30.0	4.0
C	50.0	3.0
	100.0	

A *man inside the stadium is seen with the stub of a free pass.*
What is the probability that he came through turnstile A, through
turnstile B, through turnstile C?

Again, there are at least two ways of solving this problem.

Method 1. Express the percents as numbers of people using each
turnstile. Assume that 1,000 people came into the stadium. This means
that 200 passed through turnstile A (20.0 percent of 1,000); 300 through
B; and 500 through C.

Now change the free-pass percents to numbers.

Turnstile	Number who enter	Free passes Percent	Number
A	200	5.0	10
B	300	4.0	12
C	500	3.0	15
			37

Therefore, the probabilities are

turnstile A: 10/37
turnstile B: 12/37
turnstile C: 15/37

Method 2. Again, this method will suit those who have no difficulty in working with percents.

Turnstile	Percent who enter	Percent with free passes	Product of percents
A	20.0	5.0	100
B	30.0	4.0	120
C	50.0	3.0	150
			370

turnstile *A*: *P* = 100/370 = 10/37
turnstile *B*: *P* = 120/370 = 12/37
turnstile *C*: *P* = 150/370 = 15/37

This type of problem often appears in analyzing the products that machines make. The problem is usually this: If many machines in a factory are producing one thing, of which some are faulty, what is the probability that a certain machine produced the faulty product?

PROBLEM 15: *We close the grab bag with a double-barreled problem. It involves two basic problem types in the theory of probability. These are:*

1. The problem of picking balls of different colors from an urn. (Let's call it a jar through which you can't see.)

Since the jar contains a mixture of colored balls, the question is: What is the probability of picking out a certain number of balls of one color and so many of another?

This type of problem is met in almost every scientific field. It also comes up in almost everything having to do with human populations.

Think of your town or city. It probably contains a mixture of white and Negro people. Let us assume that the ratio is 90 white to 10 Negro. A city official has to pick possible jurors for trials. What is the probability that the jury list will contain the proportion of white and Negro nearly the way it exists in the total population? Jury lists are usually chosen by chance, or randomly, a new word of very great importance that will be discussed in the next chapter.

This question — of jury lists resembling the proportions of the general population — is so important that it has even gone to the United States Supreme Court.

2. The second part of the problem deals with this: After we have taken a ball from the jar, we have two choices of what to do. We can keep the ball out of the jar and make our next pick. The other choice is to note the color of the ball and throw it back into the jar before we pick again.

The first way is called picking without replacement.

The second way is called picking with replacement.

How does our choice of methods affect the probability?

This is, as you can see, a tough nut of a problem, but we will attack it within a simple setting.

A jar contains

4 white balls
8 black balls
12 total balls

In 6 picks, calculate the probability of taking out, in any order,

2 white balls
4 black balls
6 total balls

(*Note:* Since there is a mixture of only two kinds, black and white, we can use the formula for combinations where necessary. If the mixture contained more colors, the formula would be slightly different. We would use the formula for permutations when several things are alike, as in some of the anagram problems.)

a. *With replacement* of the balls after they have been picked and the colors noted:

$$P(2 \text{ white, } 4 \text{ black}) = 6 \ C \ 2 \times \left(\frac{4}{12}\right)^2 \times \left(\frac{8}{12}\right)^4$$

| this is really 6 things, 2 of 1 kind (white), 4 of another kind (black) | the probability of picking white twice | the probability of picking black 4 times |

Reduce the fractions.

$$\frac{6!}{2! \ 4!} \times \left(\frac{1}{3}\right)^2 \times \left(\frac{2}{3}\right)^4 = \frac{6 \times 5}{2} \times \frac{1}{9} \times \frac{16}{81} = \frac{480}{1458} = \frac{80}{243}$$

With replacement the probability of picking 2 white and 4 black balls is almost exactly 1/3, or 1 out of 3.

b. *Without replacement*, the formula must consider:

1. Ways of taking 2 balls out of 4 (white) = 4 C 2
2. Ways of taking 4 balls out of 8 (black) = 8 C 4
3. Ways of taking 6 balls out of 12 (total of all) = 12 C 6

Then P (2 white, 4 black) =

$\dfrac{\text{step } 1 \times \text{step } 2}{\text{step } 3}$ (This is the proportion of all possible combinations that we will use.)

$$\dfrac{\dfrac{4!}{2! \ 2!} \times \dfrac{8!}{4! \ 4!}}{\dfrac{12!}{6! \ 6!}} = \dfrac{6 \times 70}{924} = \dfrac{420}{924} = \dfrac{5}{11}$$

Without replacement, the probability has gone up to 5/11 or almost 1/2. This is quite an increase in the probability.

4 SAMPLING

ON THE SCREEN of a movie house flash the words: COMING ATTRACTIONS. Three short scenes from next week's picture follow. Altogether, they last five minutes. After they are over, a boy says to his friend, "It doesn't look so hot to me."

On the basis of a 5 percent sample (5 minutes of a movie that will run 100 minutes), he has made up his mind. Although he does not think of it that way, as far as he is concerned, he is a sampling expert.

A girl's room is to be redecorated. In preparation, her mother has visited a fabric store. There she was given small pieces of various materials (called "swatches") from which the girl will choose one for a bedspread. The girl picks out one swatch and says, "I like this."

The piece of material may be only 2 × 2 inches. The material for the spread will be hundreds of times as large. The girl doesn't ask, "Will the larger piece look like this?" From a small sample that showed the basic pattern, she reached a conclusion about the larger whole. She, too, is a sampling expert.

When your mother tastes a spoonful of soup or stew that she is making and says, "Mmm. This is good. You'll love it," she, too, is a sampling expert. The family usually trusts her judgment.

Sampling is so much a part of our life that its meaning is understood by almost everyone. It is the act of reaching a decision or making a judgment about the whole of something on the basis of study or examination of a small part.

In statistics, too, we reach conclusions or form opinions or make important decisions on the basis of a sample. It is far more difficult (and a lot less pleasant) to select a statistical sample and reach a correct conclusion than to taste soup. But the methods have been so perfected that we can be just as certain in our conclusions.

The process of making decisions about large groups of things on the basis of small samples is called *statistical inference*. It is probably the most important field of practical statistical work.

In human affairs, the use of sampling is so common that almost no field of activity—government, business, education, industry, science—could get along without it. How many people are unemployed? The federal government finds out by means of a sample. How many lanes of traffic should a proposed bridge have? The answer may come from a sample of possible users. Small parts are produced by a machine in thousands per day. The company wants to know whether they meet its standards. A sample of these parts will supply the answer. Who is likely to win the next election? A group of men will use a sample of possible voters to try to answer the question. A research laboratory believes that it has developed a drug to cure a disease. A sample of mice or men will help decide whether this is so.

A census is a complete count. A sample is a partial count of *scientifically chosen units* of what would be included in a census. In using a sample rather than a census, we are not settling for "second best." By means of a sample, it is possible to obtain as accurate and precise information as is desired. Most often, when the attempt is made to count everything, we don't completely succeed. Some things are left out. Others are counted twice. As we shall see in the story of the census, counting is not easy, especially in great amounts.

When and why do we sample?

1. A sample is used when a test of the total product is *destructive:* the test destroys the thing being tested.

If your mother, instead of sampling the soup, had finished the whole pot and said, "Mmm. This is good," the rest of the family might have said sarcastically, "Thanks for the information." As far as they were concerned, she would have "destroyed" the soup.

Here are some examples from real life of destructive testing that, therefore, require small samples.

a. A man imports foreign chocolate. At the customs house, a duty (tax) will have to be paid on it, depending upon the weight. The chocolate will also be tested to see whether it meets United States health standards. According to a careful plan, a sample of chocolate is chosen for testing weight and quality. The tested chocolate is, of course, destroyed in the process.

b. A company advertises that its frozen meat pies contain at least two ounces of meat. They are made by the thousands on automatic machines. Most of the product is sold to chain stores. The company knows that the chain stores will test the pies for their meat content. They will be sent back if they do not contain the minimum amount. Also, a government inspector may call to test the company's advertised claim. Therefore, the company will test its own pies for meat content. Each tester will use a small sample because to test is to destroy.

c. A rocket's final test is in the firing. To test is to destroy. Therefore, a small sample of rockets will be fired to test accuracy, distance, misfires, etc.

d. To test how long a light bulb will burn means to burn it.

e. To test how strong a fabric is means trying to tear it or to wear it out.

f. To test how many miles per gallon a new gasoline will

give means to burn the gasoline in cars of different weight and engine size.

In all these cases, samples will give the required answers.

2. A sample is used when *time* is an important element in the decision to be made.

a. The government has to know at all times how many people are unemployed; whether most of the unemployed are young or old, men or women, Negro or white. Important decisions depend upon changes in the number of persons without jobs. The information is needed quickly so that action can be taken, if necessary. A sharp rise in unemployment may call for one course of action. A sharp drop may be a signal that expensive government programs can be dropped. If the government had to wait for a census of people without jobs, the situation might quickly go from bad to worse. Quick and accurate information may be obtained by sampling.

b. Let us assume that a presidential campaign is under way. One candidate wants to know how people feel about government aid to education. He asks a polling organization (a group that samples opinions of possible voters) to find out for him. Depending upon their findings, he will either make or not make an important speech about that subject. The findings will be based upon a sample.

c. Television broadcasters regularly use samples of listeners to find out which are the most popular programs.

d. A company with a stock of more than 10,000 different items on hand has to take an inventory (a count of how much it has of different goods in its store, warehouse, or factory) for tax purposes. It uses a sample of its stock to find out.

In all the above cases time is important and information is obtained quickly by means of a sample.

3. A sample is used when it is clear that everything can't possibly be counted, even if there were a desire to do so.

a. Any study of coin-tossing must be based upon a sample. There is no end to tossing coins. If one coin or one thousand coins were tossed every day for a lifetime, there would still remain an untossed coin. All tests or trials that *resemble* coin-tossing must use a sample.

b. A biologist testing the growth, or lack of growth, of bacteria with a new drug uses a sample to check his results. Such an experiment could go on forever.

c. The results of measuring the same thing—the thickness of a copper wire, the angle of a layer of rock—are found by means of a sample. Measurement can continue until the instruments wear out.

d. A geologist is told by an oil company to bring back shale to test its oil content. He would be a geologist without a job if he brought back the mountain. Being wise, he returns with a sample.

e. In one of the states, fishermen complain to their Conservation Department that trout in the lakes are disappearing. There are 3 possibilities: (1) the trout are really disappearing, (2) there are more of other fish so that trout are harder to catch, and (3) the fishermen today are not as good as those of other years. The department decides to make a study. Obviously, it cannot count the trout in the lakes. It could, perhaps, drain the lakes and take a census. But that would be like mother finishing the pot of soup. The fishermen then could say, "Thanks. You've really been a big help." Instead, the department could proceed as follows: Each year, perhaps for five years, at the same time of the year, at the same time of day, with the same size nets, at the same place, it could catch a sample of fish and count them.

In 1964, there were complaints that the fish in the Mississippi River were dying in great numbers. The U.S. Public Health Service took a sample. It found that pesticides (chemicals used to kill plant-destroying insects) were washing into the waters and were probably responsible for killing the fish.

4. A sample is used when the information that is wanted is very technical or complicated and great accuracy is necessary.

It may seem strange that an incomplete count (a sample) could be more accurate than a complete count. Yet, in many cases, this is so. A sample can be more carefully controlled than a census. Duplication (counting the same thing twice) can be avoided. It is also easier to include everything that should be included. In a census, with its much larger numbers, this is more difficult. Also, as was said earlier, counting is not easy. More important, in sampling, expert enumerators can be used. The people who will collect the information can be well-trained. In a census, some of the people who collect the information may not be as capable. But they may have to be used because so many are needed.

Suppose that a Department of Health is planning to make a study of the health of people fifty years of age and over. It will do this by obtaining a health history covering several years. The questions will be technical but will be explained to people in simple language. All information will be obtained by visiting people at home.

It is clear that the person who asks the questions and writes down the answers must have some expert knowledge. Otherwise, the information may turn out to be useless, whether census or sample. People with such skills who are available to work on such surveys are not easily found. A census would require a large number of them. Therefore, the study is done by means of a sample.

5. A sample is used when the test or trial involves very great danger.

Sometimes, the final test of a drug, which may be very dangerous, must be on human beings. In such cases, volunteer prisoners may be used as a sample.

6. Finally, we come to a very basic reason for using a sample rather than a census. It affects all the "why and when" reasons mentioned above. That reason is *money.* Money is an important factor in all studies. Whenever a study or survey or test or trial is being discussed, two questions must be answered: (a) What do we want to find out? and (b) How much will it cost? Money not only affects the choice of sample or census; it helps decide the *kind* of sample to use; and it always affects the *size* of the sample.

The element of cost is important whether the user of the

sample is a big business, a research organization, or a government. It may seem to some that the government has an unlimited amount of money with which to conduct surveys or make studies. But this writer, who has taken part in many government studies, knows that the question, "How much will it cost?" must be answered before any study begins.

After saying, "Counting is not easy," we can now add, "Counting is expensive." Exactly how difficult and how expensive it is to count, we will see from a brief history of the census.

The Census in History

From very ancient times, man has wanted to know how many others like him there were. The strange thing is that until very recent times he never really knew. He tried often to count the people in his city, state, or nation, but the number of people shown in records that have come down to us from the past are not very accurate. Even today in a country such as the United States, which has excellent means of communication, which spends a tremendous amount of money, and which uses the latest electronic computers, the result of the census of population is not an exact count. However, so much more is known today about the problems of census-taking that we accept the results as the best that can be obtained.

The reading of this brief history of the census will be easier if some technical terms are explained.

Census: The word is commonly used to mean a complete count of every person in a country. However, there can be a census of a state or a village. There can be a complete count of anything; when there is, it is called a census. There is a census of manufactures; there is a census of agriculture. There can be a census of two-family houses. As long as the unit to be counted is named and a complete count is made, it is called a census.

Enumeration: When the unit of counting is *people,* a complete count is more precisely called an *enumeration*. An enumeration means a numbering. The U.S. Bureau of the Census, which counts the American people every tenth year—in years ending with 0—calls the census an enumeration. Before the count is made, the country is divided into *enumeration districts*. This word will be used often as a substitute for the word census.

Enumerator: An *enumerator* is the person who actually does the counting of the people. This is the man or woman who represents the Bureau of the Census during the census of population.

Population: When the word *population* is used in ordinary conversation, it refers to the people of a place. Thus, a great part of the population of New York City lives in apartment houses.

In statistics, population has a broader meaning. When we count everything, we are counting the population. The population may be people, bicycles, television sets, anything. The population is the *whole* of anything, whether a small group or the stars. If *all* red-headed astronomers in the United States were counted, there might be a *population* of fifty. If five of them were women, the population of red-headed women astronomers in the United States would be five.

The thing we are counting must be clearly defined, and all must be included in the count. Then we have a population.

On the basis of a sample, we *estimate* the population. Without actually counting, we form an idea, or reach a conclusion, about the population. The population is the body from which the sample is drawn in the first place.

In this history of the census, the population will be people. In the later discussion of sampling, the population may be anything.

Back to the story.

A census of population is an attempt to count people. But who are people? This may sound silly. However, until quite recent times, the idea of who were people was entirely different from ours. Perhaps you have read translations of stories of ancient times. The storyteller may say, "The tribe was wealthy and powerful. It numbered 10,000, and there were 2,000 head of cattle."

The count of cattle may be accurate, but the count of people never is in these ancient tales. Slaves were never counted. Even women and children were often not included. Sometimes the sick and old were omitted. Paupers (poor people with no property) were often not included. Usually, only men who paid taxes or who could serve as soldiers were included in a census of population.

There exist records of censuses of population or agriculture from ancient Babylonia, as far back as 3000 B.C. The Persian Empire, ancient China, and Egypt have also left records of population counts. But all were made for purposes of taxation or for fixing debts of money or work owed to the ruler. Many were surveys for the purpose of counting possible soldiers. From these records, some *idea* may be gotten of how large the nations were, but it is a very inexact idea. Even to get this, one must know: *Who* had to pay taxes? At *what age* did a man enter the army? *How large* were families at that time? *How many* slaves did the kingdom have?

One of the clearest accounts of a census in ancient times is in the Bible. It is mentioned in the Old Testament, Chapter XXIV of the Second Book of Samuel. The count took place more than 1000 years B.C., when King David ruled over Israel.

The story is important because it makes clear the inexactness mentioned above. Much more important, however, is the effect it has had upon census-taking to our own day.

The Bible relates that King David said to Joab, captain of the armies, "Go now through all the tribes of Israel . . . and number ye the people, that I may know the number of the people."

Joab knew that this was an affront to the Lord. He said to King David, "Now the Lord thy God add unto the people, how many soever they be, an hundredfold, and that the eyes of my lord the king may see it: but why doth my lord the king delight in this thing?"

But King David insisted.

Joab and the captains of the army went out to count the people. They returned nine months and twenty days later.

The Bible then says, "And Joab gave up the sum of the number of the people unto the king: and there were in Israel eight hundred thousand valiant men that drew the sword; and the men of Judah were five hundred thousand men."

For this sin that King David had committed, God sent a plague upon the people of Israel.

The first thing that strikes the reader is that King David had said, "Number ye the people." But the report to him by Joab mentions "eight hundred thousand valiant men that drew the sword." Only fighting men were counted. Uncounted were the women and children, those too old or too young to fight, the sick, the slaves. The uncounted were greater in number than the counted. But how many were there? The answer can be only a guess.

According to this Biblical story, "to number the people" was to sin in the eyes of the Lord. This attitude lasted for a very long time among many people. In later years, in many parts of the world, *households* were counted instead of the number of people in them. This was easier to do and not as likely to stir up ancient feelings against counting people.

This feeling is still found today among primitive tribes in Asia and Africa. Tribes living in the remote parts of these continents have fought against attempts to count them. When some of the new nations tried to take their first census, the enumerators were either killed or driven off.

The Romans

The Romans were the first to count their people on a regular basis. The word *census* comes from the Latin word *censere* — to tax. The Romans were excellent planners and organizers in most things, and their organization of census-taking was typical of them. Roman magistrates called *censors* had the special task of conducting the count of people. In a sense, they formed a special, trained organization that counted the Roman people every five years.

Just before the beginning of the Christian era, in 5 B.C., the Emperor Augustus tried to take a census of the entire Roman Empire. At that time, this included the whole civilized world. Such an ambitious plan was not carried out until very recent times.

The main purposes of the Roman census were:

1. To decide each person's position as a citizen. To be a Roman citizen was a matter of great pride and importance.

2. To decide how much taxes a man owed or could afford to pay.

This last purpose affected the accuracy of the census at that time and in other countries for many years to come. People hid or fled from the tax collector and were never counted.

In history, the Roman census is important because it was done on a regular basis by a special organization set up to carry it out.

Why count people?

Many persons may wonder why it is so important that a government make an accurate count of its people on a regular basis. In the seventeenth century, an Englishman, John Graunt, stated the main reasons with remarkable vision. He wrote, "Trade, and Government may be made more certain and Regular; for, if men knew the People . . . they might know the consumption they would make. . . . a clear knowledge . . . is necessary in order to good, certain, and easie Government."

The changes in the population, as shown by a census, help a government plan. Every government must plan for schools, homes, parks, hospitals, tax income, and many other things.

Business and industry, too, must plan ahead. It takes time and a great deal of money to build a new steel mill or auto factory. Plans for such large projects are made on the basis of expected growth of the population. Only a regular census can show this.

The U.S. Bureau of the Census reports its findings in great detail. Its publications are bought in great numbers by industry and state and local governments. They rely upon these reports to plan their programs.

In the United States, census-taking is based upon the constitution. The number of representatives in Congress from each of the states depends upon its population as shown by the census. Much of the money that the federal government distributes to the states is based upon their populations.

The two most ancient reasons for counting people are still true today:

1. To make an accurate estimate of fighting men.

2. To help estimate the amount of taxes that may be collected.

No modern government can function efficiently without an accurate count of its people. It may even be said that a nation's ability to conduct a census is an indication of how advanced it is. In England, the census has been taken every ten years since it was made a requirement of law in 1801. Turkey, on the other hand, held its first census in 1927. Denmark made its Statistical Bureau a regular part of the government in 1850 and had conducted censuses for many years before that. On the other hand, many of the new nations of Asia and Africa do not today have the necessary trained people to conduct a census. For some of them, the United Nations has helped to estimate the population.

Statisticians have a very special need for censuses of all kinds. It was said that from samples, statisticians make estimates about the "whole," or the population. Sooner or later, many of these estimates must be checked. The most common check is based upon the results of the census. The census counts in each group (age, sex, Negro, white, etc.) become *benchmarks*. A benchmark is like a landmark. It serves as a check or guide. Each group or sub-group of the census of population, manufactures, or agriculture may be a benchmark for some statistician carrying out an important study.

In the modern world the census is an all-important tool.

The final reason for census-taking may rightly be considered more important than any of these. Under proper conditions, a nation's greatest wealth is its people.

After the Romans

For many centuries after Rome fell, there is almost no mention of a census anywhere. There are records of counts of land, cattle, and other goods. These were measures of wealth and the basis for taxation. Many kings in many lands enforced such counts.

At the time of the Renaissance, in the fifteenth and sixteenth centuries, new interest arose in taking a census of population. There are records of enumerations in the great city-states of Venice and Florence, as mentioned earlier. King Philip II of Spain had a census taken in the lands that Spain had conquered. Writers in France and England wrote about the need to take a census.

One of the most fascinating of these accounts was written by the Englishman, John Graunt (1620–1674). He was a tradesman in London, who spent his spare time studying birth and death records. In a small book that he wrote, he made many points that are as important today as they were then.

"It may be asked," he wrote, "to what purpose tends all this laborious buzzling and groping? To know,

1. The number of People
2. How many Males and Females
3. How many Married and Single
4. How many fighting men
5. How much London is and by what steps it hath increased."

He also asked for a census of land and cattle and other goods. But he added: "It is no less necessary to know how many People there be of each Sex, State, Age, Religion, Trade, Rank, or Degree, and by the knowledge whereof Trade, and Government may be made more certain and Regular."

John Graunt was asking for a modern census. He was later honored for his work when King Charles II nominated him to the Royal Society.

The earliest record of a really complete census of population comes from Canada. It was taken in 1663 and repeated in 1666. At that time, the country was called New France. The records of the census described the population by sex, age, married and unmarried, and the profession or trade of the person. The total population in 1666 was 3,215!

The census in France

France is a country with a very long history. It had been conquered and ruled by the Romans. From them the French inherited a strong government and the knowledge of how to administer a country. But, for centuries, there was nothing that resembled the Roman census. The difficulties faced by the French are typical of those faced by many other countries. Despite their success in taking a census in their Canadian colony, it was not until the twentieth century that an accurate census was taken in France itself.

As early as the eighth century, at the time of the Emperor Charlemagne, a complete census of land was taken. Even the lands of the king and the church were included, a rare thing for that day. In later centuries, counts of households were made. From these two counts—lands and households—attempts were made to estimate the number of people.

By the thirteenth and fourteenth centuries, it was usual for skilled workers (shoemakers, blacksmiths, etc.) to belong to special organizations of their own called guilds. This made it possible to count their membership, and many records exist of such counts.

In those days, churches sometimes counted the population in their parishes. There are many records of such counts.

Up until the seventeenth century, households were counted a few times. This count was important because it formed the basis of a tax list. But even as in Biblical times, those left out were greater in number than those included.

Paupers were not counted. Serfs (the many who worked land but did not own it) were excluded. Nobles and soldiers and those who had been freed from paying taxes by order of the king were also omitted.

Later, King Louis XIV (1638–1715) attempted to take a census. In each province, the king's *intendant* (representative) was in charge. Some intendants counted people; some counted households; some counted only tax-paying households; some just copied their old records. Since the intendants also collected taxes, and many were dishonest, the result of their counting was almost meaningless.

After the French Revolution of 1789, the new government recognized the need for an accurate census. The great scientist, Lavoisier, was asked to prepare a plan. He did but was executed shortly thereafter, and the plan was never carried out.

In 1802, the famous mathematician, Laplace, convinced the government of the need for a census. This was carried out, but the results were poor. Using the census reports, along with birth and death records, Laplace made his own estimate of the French population. He placed it at 28,000,000. He stated that he was willing to bet that it was not wrong by more than 500,-000. No one was willing to bet, but there are indications that Laplace later lost confidence in his own estimate.

From 1836 until the end of the nineteenth century, three other attempts were made to count the population without great success. In 1901, census-taking was organized along modern lines. For this purpose, a special branch of the government was established, whose main responsibility was to count the people.

Today, France conducts a census every five years. In years ending in one, population counts are important. In years ending in six, the emphasis is on industry and occupation.

The census in Russia

This very brief outline of the history of the census in Russia is meant to illustrate two points:

1. Who conducts the census is important for an accurate count.

2. A government must be willing to pay for a census if it is to succeed.

From very early times, all statistics in Russia were under the control of the police. Even into the nineteenth century, the Minister of Police was supposed to supervise the taking of the census. None was ever really held. The authority was later transferred to the Minister of the Interior. But in Russia, as well as in many other countries, this minister is in charge of the secret police. Thus, there was really no change.

The government discussed the need for a census in 1870, but year after year, the Duma (the Congress) would not make money available for it. The discussion continued without results. The census did not get under way until 1897! It was not until 1905, thirty-five years after the idea was first discussed, that some statistics were published. They were very poor ones.

It is possible to say that never in its pre-Communist history, before 1917, did Russian rulers know exactly how many people their country held. The strangest part of this story is that some of the world's leading mathematicians were Russians!

Since the Communist Revolution, there have been several successful censuses in the Soviet Union.

The census in American history

Article 1, Section 2, of the Constitution of the United States says: "Representatives and direct taxes shall be apportioned among the several States which may be included within this Union, according to their respective numbers."

This is the legal basis for the American census of population. Many scholars claim that the makers of the Constitution were not interested in a census for its own sake. They were interested in two things:

1. Placing the payment of taxes on a fair basis.

2. Making certain that the states would always be represented fairly in the Congress.

These two points are directly tied to one of the important slogans of the Revolutionary War: No taxation without representation.

In order to carry out these purposes, an exact count of the people was necessary. In this way, the American census was born. The new country was the first one in the world to require by law that a census be taken. The first was taken in 1790, and every ten years since then the American people have been counted.

Whether the makers of the Constitution intended it or not, their reasons for a census made it possible to take an *accurate* census. On the one hand, people might want to *avoid the census* to lower their taxes. On the other hand, they *wanted to be counted* to have more representatives in Congress. Today, the second reason plays a more important part.

Thomas Jefferson, as Secretary of State under President George Washington, was director of the first census. The official enumerators were United States marshals and their assistants. There were no government forms or papers; the marshals used their own stationery to report the results. It took eighteen months to count the people. The cost was about $45,000. This was a great deal of money for a young country with many debts to pay. The official count showed about 3,900,000 people.

It was said earlier in this section that the question, "Who are people?" had different answers at different times in history. This is the way the first American census was reported:

I. FREE PEOPLE				II. SLAVES
A. White			B. Others	
1. Male		2. Female		
a. Under 16	b. Over 16			

Slaves, who were property, were not counted by sex or age. But the fact that they were counted at all may be a sign of the democratic thinking of the time. White people were counted by sex. But only free white men were also counted by age. The first census was, then, a mixture of old and new ideas. This census was still a family-type (household) census, but the attempt was made to count individuals.

The census changed with experience and new ideas. By 1820, slaves were also counted by sex and age. Official printed forms came into use in 1830. In the 1850 census, families and households were no longer counted. The object of the census was the individual person. It was in this census, also, that the reports from all parts of the country were first collected in a central office in Washington.

There was not yet, however, a permanent census office. Before each census, a new chief (Superintendent of the Census) was appointed. Often, he was a man with no special training for the job. And the marshals and their assistants still collected the information.

The census of 1880 was an important turning point. It is often called the first modern census. Although marshals still were used, civilian enumerators were also employed. And, for the first time, there were civilian supervisors in charge of the marshals.

By 1902–1903, the Bureau of the Census became a permanent office. It was placed in the Department of Commerce, where it still is today.

In 1940, one hundred and fifty years after the first census, sampling was used for the first time. Of course, all the people were counted and asked the important questions about age, sex, race, etc. But other questions were asked of only a sample of people. Sampling was used for the question of housing in the 1950 and 1960 censuses as well. Although the population will always be counted, it is likely that sampling will be used more and more for other questions in the future.

Counting is not easy, as we have said. Even the best census

contains errors. With the increase in knowledge, however, it is now possible to estimate the *kinds* and *sizes* of errors in a census. The Bureau of the Census makes its own analysis of the errors in its count.

Today, every census is immediately followed by a post-enumeration study. This may take the form of an extremely careful recount in a few areas by the best enumerators. By this and other methods, the Bureau of the Census will estimate the errors.

The errors may be in the total count of the population. They may be in an age group, in the count of male and female, in the Negro population. One common error is in the count by age. It has been found that many people "round out" their age to end in zero or five. A woman of thirty-three may give her age as thirty. A man of sixty-four may tell the enumerator that he is sixty-five. Such errors are difficult to check or to correct.

The 1950 census has been carefully studied by statisticians in the Bureau of the Census as well as by independent scholars. That census reported the population to be approximately 151,000,000. After its post-enumeration study, the Bureau of the Census stated that there had been an undercount of 3.0 percent. This would be about 5,000,000 people.

Professor Ansley J. Coale of Princeton University also made a study of this census. He reported that the error was probably nearer to 5.0 percent. Remember that a 1.0 percent error means more than 1,500,000 people. His article, which appeared in the March, 1955, issue of the *Journal of the American Statistical Association,* opens with these words: "It is clear to all who consider the question that data from the U.S. decennial censuses of population are less than perfect. Persons who should be included are omitted, others are counted twice, and characteristics of the persons included are sometimes misreported."

Any remarks made or quoted by this author are not meant as criticisms of the Bureau of the Census. It is, in fact, one of the best in the world. They are mentioned as proof that counting is not easy. Two important reasons for error will make this clear.

1. Many years ago an exact enumeration was made more difficult because communications, especially roads, were poor. People were hard to reach. Today, however, with greatly improved means of transportation, census-taking has become even more complicated. A man may be counted in California in the morning. A few hours later he may be in New York City. That evening he may be in a London hotel. The American people are always on the move.

For a large part of the population, movement is a way of life. Some don't even have a permanent home. There are migrant farm workers who move from state to state with their families to harvest crops. Construction workers travel over the land putting up bridges, digging tunnels, building roads. In many cases, their home is a trailer. Other people live in boarding or rooming houses or hotels. They, also, move from place to place. Such people are hard to count accurately.

2. To conduct a modern census in a country as large as the United States requires a tremendous number of enumerators. About 240,000 enumerators were used in the 1960 census. This is equal to the population of a good-sized city. The job of enumerator lasts for only a few months, at most. The pay is very modest. There are bound to be many who do a careless job. Their ability or interest or public spirit is not high enough. The Bureau of the Census checks on their work, but it is humanly impossible to check in great detail the work of 240,000 people.

The census could possibly be made more accurate, but the increase in cost would be enormous. Congress, which makes available the necessary money, might not think it worthwhile.

This brings up the second point made earlier. Counting is expensive. Exactly how expensive may be seen from the cost of the 1960 census.

This enumeration began on April 1 of that year. But before

the start, over 1,000,000 man-hours had been spent in planning and preparation. The many enumerators had to be paid. It was the first census to make large-scale use of electronic computers. By July 7 of the same year, about three months after it had begun, the complete census count (but not details) was reported. The cost? Almost $130,000,000!

The basis of a modern census

Conducting a modern census is a very complicated task. Throughout history, attempts at it have failed for one or more reasons. From a study of the successes and failures, these would seem to be the main requirements for an accurate census:

1. A stable population—one not likely to rise or fall suddenly

European civilization reached a high point centuries ago, but wars between countries continued almost without end. This meant not only that many were killed and many starved but also that huge areas, with their people, very often changed from control by one kingdom to control by another.

Religious persecution also caused large numbers of people to flee. This was one reason for the settlement of the American colonies.

Widespread plagues often killed millions of people even into the seventeenth century.

2. A stable government

With nations constantly at war or threatened by it, governments changing, kings being murdered, their thrones usurped, and revolutions carried out, there could be no planning for a census. Also, under such conditions, money is not likely to be made available for accurate census-taking.

3. Good communications, especially roads

Despite the difficulties that excellent modern transportation creates, good roads are still vital for a census. Indians in the jungles of Brazil are hard to reach. Nomads in the deserts of the Arab world may never be reached by a census-taker. A census, to be accurate, cannot be drawn out over too long a time.

4. Trained experts to plan and conduct the census

Even today, in many countries, there has been neither time nor money available to train experts to conduct a census. This is especially true of the new nations in Asia and Africa. For many of these, the United Nations has made estimates of their population, using experts from the more advanced countries.

The idea that experts are needed to conduct a census is a modern one. In most advanced countries, including the United States, a permanent office of government responsible for a census came into existence in the twentieth century.

5. Confidence in the government

This does not mean that everybody must agree that it is a "good" government, but people must believe that the information given to the enumerator will not be used against them in any way. Otherwise, many may be inclined to lie to him.

A tax-collector has never been a good census-taker. Too many people lied to him or ran away from him. In European countries, when it was suspected that the census-taker was really counting possible soldiers, many people hid from him. Policemen, also, have never taken an accurate census.

Aside from people's fear or mistrust of them, tax-collectors, army men, policemen, all were trained for other duties. Counting people was not their main task or interest.

The taking of a census must be a full-time responsibility of a branch of the government created to do just that.

Scientific Sampling

Modern census-taking is costly, takes time, and involves many trained people. With all this, a census has errors that cannot be avoided. In modern society, life is complicated. The counting of people requires scientific methods and machinery such as the electronic computer. These make it possible to complete a count more quickly and accurately and then to estimate the errors.

A sample, scientifically chosen, can give accurate information about the population from which it is taken. A sample must stand on its own feet; it is not simply a substitute for a census. *A sample is a child of the laws of probability.*

In statistics, the first division into types of samples is between large and small. Small samples are those with less than thirty cases. This section will deal with large samples, except for one special case. Small samples require the use of statistical tables that are outside the range of this book.

Different situations, or studies, call for different types and sizes of samples. However, any sample, to be considered scientific, must tell an interested person two things:

1. *Exactly how accurate the statistic is that the sample has measured.* The statistic may be an average of the weekly wages of auto mechanics in Chicago. Suppose that, by means of a sample, this is found to be $100 per week. But the interest is not in the wages of the mechanics in the sample; it is in the wages of *all* auto mechanics in Chicago—the population. Therefore, it is said, "Auto mechanics in Chicago earn, on the average, $100 per week," as if a census had been taken.

If a census really had been taken, the average might be somewhat different. This, however, will never be known because a census is not being taken. But it is possible to calculate *the difference between the average of the sample and the probable average of the population* of mechanics. *This is the heart of the sampling process.*

This difference is called the *standard error of the mean.* It is shown by the symbol $\sigma \bar{X}$. If the standard error of the mean is $3, it tells us that the *real* average of wages of mechanics in Chicago is probably between $97 and $103 ($100 plus or minus $3).

This "error" is not a mistake. It is a result of the act of using a sample. If the sample were increased in size, with more mechanics included, the "error" could be reduced to $2 or $1. The size of the "error" is often set in advance of a study by the degree of accuracy needed by the user.

The "error" may be stated in absolute amounts ($3) or as a percent. In this example, it would be 3.0 percent ($100 in wages; a standard error of the mean of $3).

2. *How much confidence people can have in the results.* This is usually stated in the following way: There are 95 chances out of 100 that the true average, if it came from a census, would not differ from the average of this sample by a certain amount. The amount could be $3 or 3.0 percent—whatever the calculations show it to be.

The degree, or level, of confidence can be made as strict as desired. It may be "99 chances out of 100" or "997 chances out of 1,000." The level of confidence also depends upon the user of the statistic. An increase in the size of the sample will usually increase the level of confidence.

If the results of a sample cannot tell a reader these two things, it is not a scientific sample. Anyone interested enough should be able to check on the sample.

The results of scientific experiments are reported in the same way. Can you imagine a medical scientist reporting the results of an experiment with a new drug as follows? "I gave some of the pink medicine to a bunch of patients. Some were helped a lot by it. Others got a little help. Some, I'm sorry to say, did not do so well."

Even a cake recipe reported this way would be laughed at.

He would have to report *exactly* what he gave, *exactly* in what amounts, *exactly* how many received it, *exactly* how many were helped, and *exactly* what the degree of help was.

The idea is that anyone reading the report of an experiment or of a sample should be able to repeat it. The results obtained by anyone else should be within a certain *range* of error a certain number of times, if not every time.

Little sampling, less science

The most unscientific samples sometimes sound as if they were superscientific. They may sometimes be used because there is no other way of obtaining information. They may be used by people with little knowledge. Sometimes, however, they are used to deceive people.

They may do little harm if they are not passed off as scientific. There are times when they provide some information when there would otherwise be none.

Example of an unscientific sample

Two young friends are walking through a botanic garden. They come to a flower bed in full bloom. One says to the other, "Hey! I'll bet there are about a million flowers here."

The other agrees that there are a lot but will not agree to a million. Since they can't count all the flowers, they decide to try to estimate the number by sampling. (See the diagram below.)

They measure the flower bed by their footsteps. It is 10

SAMPLING IN A FLOWER BED
An example and a model

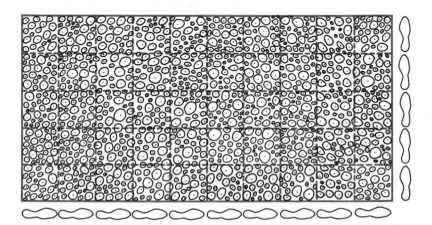

"feet" by 5 "feet," or 50 square "feet" (10 × 5). Therefore, there are 50 "boxes," each 1 "foot" square. They are confident that they can "keep their eye" on a box this size.

They decide to count the flowers in 2 corner boxes and then multiply by 25 (25 × 2 = 50). In this way, they will estimate the total number of flowers in the bed.

To make the sample more "scientific," they decide that any flower more than half in the box will count as "in the box."

Their results are: 19 flowers in one box; 21 in the other. Multiplying the total (40) by 25, they now estimate that there are 1,000 flowers in the bed.

This is an enormous improvement over "I'll bet there are a million!" and over no knowledge at all. In this sense, the two friends now have more information. And they would certainly be very bright to think up this solution to the problem.

But how precise is their information? Can they answer the two basic questions?

1. What is the size of the error in their sampling estimate of 1,000 flowers?

2. How much confidence can we have in their results?

There are two important reasons why their sample was not scientific.

1. The unit of measurement (2 squares, 1 "foot" by 1 "foot") was very inexact. They recognized it only by "keeping their eye" on it.

2. The corner squares in their sample may have been very special ones. Perhaps flowers grew there more densely or more sparsely than in the center of a bed. Their 2-square average was 20 flowers per square (21 + 19)/2. The true average may have been 15 or 25. There was no way to find out from their results.

Although this is not a scientific way of sampling, it is, unfortunately, used very often. The pattern of these squares is of a type that is often met. Look at the diagram one way: The squares could be the states of the United States. Another way, they could be the blocks of a city. They could be the apartments in an apartment house. They could be cartons stacked in a factory. They could be experimental plots of land at an agricultural testing station.

Can the flowers be counted by a scientific sample? They can, as will be shown later. If the need for precise information was great enough and could not be obtained in any other way, an aerial photograph could be taken and the enlargement divided into squares.

We are surrounded by unscientific samples that try to estimate many things. Many opinion polls on important issues are no more scientific than the flower-bed example. Newspaper polls of the opinion of the "average man" are little better. Television ads that say, "One out of four doctors recommends Dandy Drops," are based on even less scientific samples.

Examples of scientific samples

In a scientific experiment, all the elements must be strictly controlled. If they are not, if they become contaminated, the scientist cannot measure or describe his results. The same is true of any statistical study based upon a sample.

Because sampling is the heart of statistical work, some space will be devoted to describing a practical problem involving sampling. It may also serve to give you a feeling for the way a statistician approaches a problem.

Problem: A government agency has to find out the average weekly payroll (how much is paid out in wages) in retail food establishments.

This is a common type of problem. In one form or another, payroll, wages, income, and the like are the objects of study by private as well as government agencies.

The problem, as stated above, seems to be a very simple one, but the selection of a scientific sample is only one step in its solution. Before that, here are some of the questions that would have to be answered:

What is a food establishment?

Everyone would agree on a grocery store or supermarket;

also, probably, upon fruit and vegetable stores, bread and cake stores. But what about the men who sell these things from trucks, especially in suburban areas? Should stores that sell only candy be included? What about candy stands in movie houses? Popcorn or custard stands? Liquor stores? What should be done about a food club that sells fancy fruits or jams and jellies or health foods by mail only? Should those who fill automatic food machines be included? How do we regard restaurants? And delicatessens in which food may be eaten in the shop or taken home? A chicken farmer who sells eggs to the public?

After these and similar questions are answered, there are just as many to be asked about: *Whose wages should be included?*

Are the wages of the owner who works in his own store to be included? His wife's? His children's, who may help him? The wages of a cleaning woman who comes once each week? These are only a few.

No matter how simple or obvious it seems, *those to be included in a sample must be clearly defined.*

The purpose of the study has been stated. The units have been clearly defined. The next step is to set up a *sampling frame.*

The sampling frame includes the entire population *as it was defined.* If the answer was "No" to liquor stores, then *none* must be included. If it was "Yes" to candy stores, then *all* must be included in the sampling frame. From this frame, the sample will be chosen.

The sampling frame may consist of stores, people, nuts and bolts, long-distance telephone calls. It depends upon the purpose of the study.

The sampling frame is very often a list. In this case, it would be a list of retail food establishments. The list may be on 3″ × 5″ cards, IBM cards, sheets of paper. It doesn't matter as long as it is convenient to use. When the sampling frame is complete, the sample can be picked.

Random Numbers

One of the key words in the statistical vocabulary is *random*. It means completely by chance; without favoritism or bias; that every item in a set from which we are making a choice has an equal chance of being chosen; according to the laws of probability.

Randomness is the result of making random choices.

A scientific sample must be chosen from the sampling frame on a random basis. That this must be so will be clear if it is remembered that probability is the rock upon which sampling rests.

The great English statistician, L. H. C. Tippett, has stated the reasons for randomness very clearly in his book, *Sampling*. He wrote: "As a random sample is increased in size, it gives a result that comes closer and closer to the population value.

"Samples taken in some other ways give results that come closer and closer to some value other than the population value—a sample of this kind is said to be biased."

Tippett's statement is full of good red meat. If you digest it, you will grow in understanding of sampling theory.

Read the first part again. Doesn't this sound the same as the statement in probability that said: As we toss a coin more and more, the proportion of heads comes closer and closer to one-half—the population value?

The "population value" is the result obtained from a complete census. As the random sample is increased in size, it comes closer and closer to this value—which may be an average.

The aim is, then, to choose a random sample. How can this be done? Good intentions to be "fair" in the choosing are not enough. Human beings have favorite numbers, whether they know it or not. They also have habits that cause them to lean in certain directions. In other words, they have *bias*, or prejudice.

Suppose that you were asked 1,000 times (if you could stand it) to pick a number from 0 to 9. At the end, do you think that you would have 100 each of 0's, 1's, 2's, etc.? Never! Your favorite number or numbers would lead the list.

You may have seen someone spread out a deck of cards and say, "Pick a card." How often have you seen the person pick the top card? The very last card? Most people pick from the middle of the deck.

These two examples mean that every number from 0 to 9 and every card in the deck *did not have an equal chance of being chosen*. There was a bias as a result of habit.

Since picking a random sample involves making such choices, it cannot be left to human decision.

Sometimes the bias is hidden. We don't know that it is there until too late. And, as Tippett implies in the second part of his statement, *the larger the sample that is not random, the more obvious a bias becomes*.

This is an important concept. The larger a random sample becomes, the closer its derived measures (e.g., mean) come to the population or "true" value. A small random sample may, within the limits of probability, consist of non-typical values. This becomes more and more unlikely as the random sample increases in size.

The reverse is true of a non-random sample. A small one may, within probability limits, include typical values, but this becomes more and more unlikely as the non-random sample increases in size. The bias inherent in the non-random selection is more and more clearly exposed the longer we continue selecting a sample in a non-random — or biased — way.

The bias in such sampling is often difficult to foresee. In the early days of the draft, on the eve of World War II, an attempt was made to choose early draftees on a random basis. The methodology was that of putting numbered pellets in a bowl, mixing them, and making selections. This was not random sampling. Later analysis showed that there had been a distinct bias. Quite likely, the "mix" did not take; certain groups tended to remain on top and were more likely to be selected than others. This could only have become evident, given the large population or universe involved, as the sample grew in size.

Let us assume that the following things can be found in your home:

1. Two decks of playing cards exactly alike.
2. A mischievous little brother.

Unknown to you, your brother has taken 2 spades from one deck and substituted 2 diamonds from the second deck. You have just finished the chapter on probability and want to make an experiment. You will pick a card, replace it, mix the deck, and pick again. After many picks, you know that you should have close to ¼ of each of the suits: clubs, diamonds, hearts, and spades.

You don't know it but your deck contains

$$
\begin{array}{l}
13 \text{ clubs} \\
15 \text{ diamonds} \\
13 \text{ hearts} \\
\underline{11} \text{ spades} \\
\overline{52} \text{ total}
\end{array}
$$

After the first 40 or 50 picks, you may have close to ¼ of each suit. But as you continue to pick, the numbers reaching into the hundreds, something strange begins to happen. You are picking fewer than ¼ spades and more than ¼ diamonds. You are ready to doubt all the laws of probability. But, as a true scientist, you decide to check your materials. You discover your brother's mischief—he has introduced a hidden bias. It became clearer the more you picked, that is, the larger your sample grew.

Before describing the choosing of a random sample, here is one of the most famous stories in the history of sampling. It shows what can happen when the steps mentioned above are not followed: the sampling frame is not clearly defined; the sample is not random; there is a hidden bias.

In the 1930's, the *Literary Digest* was one of the most popular magazines in the United States. Before the 1936 election, it decided to take a poll to find out who would win. A poll is a sample of voter opinion. In that year, Franklin D. Roosevelt, Democrat, was running for the Presidency against Alfred Landon, Republican.

About 10,000,000 postcard ballots were mailed out to every part of the country. The names came from telephone books and auto registration lists. Over 2,000,000 filled-out ballots were returned to the magazine. This was probably the largest poll ever held. Today it is a rare poll that uses a list of more than 3,000 voters.

The results of the poll were: Landon—60 percent; Roosevelt—40 percent. On Election Day, the actual results were almost the exact opposite. Roosevelt received more than 60 percent of the vote in one of the biggest runaway victories in American election history.

How could this enormous sample of 2,000,000 have been so wrong?

The sampling frame was wrong. It did not consist of possible voters; it consisted of owners of telephones or cars or both. The year 1936 was one of great depression. Millions of people were out of work. At that time only 3 out of 10 homes had telephones. Today, more than 8 out of 10 have them. Car ownership was limited to people with high earnings. It is a fact of American life that such people are *more likely* to vote Republican.

A person with a high income who had both a telephone and a car had two chances of being included in the sample. A poor worker or farmer, with neither, had no chance at all. The results of the election later showed that a very high proportion of this group voted for Roosevelt. This was the hidden bias.

The poll was not a sample of possible American voters. It was a sample of telephone users and car owners.

The *Literary Digest* poll had been followed with great interest by many people. The result of the actual election was a shock. Within a few months the magazine went out of business.

The random sample: not a miracle

It may seem from all this that a random sample is only the subject of a statistician's dream, but it becomes real quite easily with a little time and effort. A random sample is picked with the help of *a table of random digits*. Here is a small section from such a table:

Line number									
00130	25163	01889	70014	15021	41290	67312	71857	15957	68971	11403
00131	65251	07629	37239	33295	05870	01119	92784	26340	18477	65622
00132	36816	43625	18637	37509	83444	99005	04921	73701	14707	93997
00133	64397	11692	05327	82162	20247	81759	45197	25332	83745	22567
00134	04515	25624	95096	67946	48460	85558	15191	18782	16930	33361

At first glance, these numbers may seem to be the scribblings of a child. They don't seem to make sense. As a matter of fact, they do and they don't.

They *don't* in the sense that there is no order.

They *do* in the sense that, being random numbers, they must follow the laws of probability. Such sets of numbers are the object of very strict tests. Among these are:

1. There must be an approximately equal number of 0's, 1's, 2's, etc.

2. Odd and even digits must tend to balance.

3. Low (0–4) and high (5–9) digits must tend to balance.

There are other, more complicated tests. Only after a set of digits has met these tests is it considered random. Don't try to test the small group of digits shown above. This is only a section of a whole.

The numbers are arranged in columns of 5 digits only for easy reading. They are usually read as you would a book— line by line and from left to right. Each line is assigned a number; in this section there are lines 130 to 134.

The English statistician, Tippett, mentioned earlier, was one of the first to prepare a set of random digits. Today, such numbers can be produced by electronic computers.

The table of random digits is used in the following way.

Assume that the population of food stores in the sampling frame consists of 100 stores. The names and addresses of these stores are printed on 3″ × 5″ cards. Each has been assigned an identification number, starting with 00 and ending with 99. From these 100 cards, a sample of 10 will be selected.

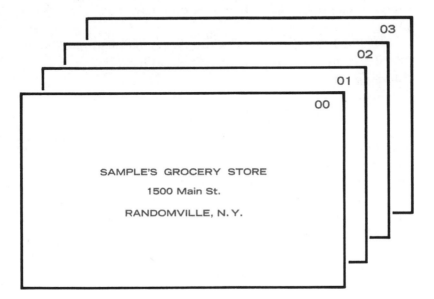

The first move is to "enter" the table of random digits to select the sample of 10 stores. The decision as to where to enter is also decided by a random process. Assume that the starting point is the fifth digit on line 00132. Since the 3″ × 5″ cards are numbered from 00 to 99, the random digits are chosen as 2-digit numbers. The first 10 pairs of numbers will be the sample. If duplicates should occur, they are ignored, and the next pair is selected.

Refer to the table of random digits. The sample consists of the cards with the following identification numbers:

54 36 25 18 63
73 75 09 82 44

Such a sample is called a *random probability sample*. It is the most fundamental sampling method. Since it is based upon the laws of probability, all necessary calculations can be made from the information obtained by means of the sample: the mean, standard deviation, the standard error of the mean, the level of confidence. The standard error of the mean from a random sample is smaller than that from any other type of sample.

(If the 1 "foot" squares of the flower bed had been numbered, a random sample of squares could have been chosen in the same way.)

The standard error of the mean ($\sigma_{\bar{x}}$)

We come now to one of the most beautiful, satisfying, and useful ideas in the field of statistics. Let us follow this idea from its simple beginning to the final design.

A sample of 10 stores has been chosen. The cards are then put back into the "deck" of 100 cards. Then another sample of the same size is chosen. Again the cards are replaced. Suppose that a great number of samples of 10 stores are selected. This can be done because the cards are replaced. After the information is collected, a mean (average) of the weekly payrolls is calculated separately for each sample of 10. There are as many means as there are samples. Some means may be alike; most will be different. Here is the beauty of it. If there are enough means and we plot them on a graph, *they will form a normal (bell-shaped) curve.* This will happen even if the population of 100 from which the samples were taken does not resemble this type of curve. See the graph on page 189.

This is known as the *central limit theorem.* It says: No matter what the shape of the original population may be, a distribution of means based on samples will tend to form a normal curve if the number in each sample is large enough.

The fact that this happens permits many important calculations to be made. For example, if we calculated the "grand"

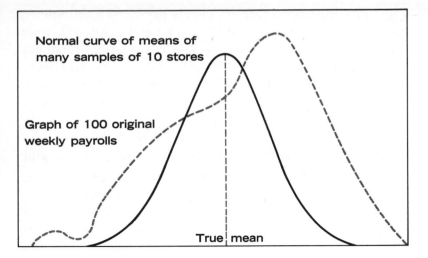

Normal curve of means of
many samples of 10 stores

Graph of 100 original
weekly payrolls

True mean

mean — an average of all the averages of the different samples —
it would tend to be equal to the "true" mean of the population
of 100.

Of course, in everyday statistical work only one sample is
chosen. There would be no point in collecting sample after
sample. It would be easier to take a census of the population.
The question then becomes: By how much does the mean of
our sample differ from the "grand" or "true" mean of the population? The amount by which it differs is called the *standard
error of the mean.*

It is calculated by a very simple formula:

$$\text{the standard} \longrightarrow \sigma_{\bar{x}} = \frac{\sigma}{\sqrt{n}} \begin{cases} \text{the standard deviation} \\ \text{of the characteristic} \\ \leftarrow \text{the square root of the} \\ \text{number in the sample} \end{cases}$$

the standard error of the mean

The size of the standard error of the mean depends upon only
two elements.

1. *The standard deviation* (σ) — *the numerator.* This measure has been discussed earlier. The size of the standard deviation is a measure of how concentrated or scattered is the char-

acteristic being studied. Here, weekly payroll in food stores is the characteristic. If the weekly payrolls of the different stores range from $5 to $500, the standard deviation will be relatively small. But if the range is from $5 to $5,000, the standard deviation will be considerably larger. This scatter, or dispersion, is technically called the *variability* of the characteristic. It means: How is this element spread out?

Since this factor is in the numerator, *the larger the standard deviation, the larger the standard error of the mean*, with the same sample size.

2. *The size of the sample* $(\sqrt{n})$ — *the denominator.* Since this is the denominator of the fraction, *the larger the size of the sample, the smaller the size of the standard error of the mean.* This is as expected. The larger the random sample, the closer it comes to the entire population. Therefore, the "error" due to sampling is likely to be lower.

The "missing member" of this formula is as interesting as those present. The size of the population from which the sample is taken has nothing to do with the size of the standard error of the mean! In the case of the food stores, the population could contain 100, 1,000, or 1,000,000 stores. But only the size of the sample is important. It is important to keep this in mind: the *variability* — the spread — of the characteristic to be studied is meaningful; the size of the population that gave birth to it is not.

With the use of this simple formula, $\sigma_{\bar{x}} = \sigma/\sqrt{n}$, it is possible to decide in advance how large a sample is needed for a study. Only two items of information are needed:

1. How large a standard error of the mean is satisfactory for the purpose of the study.

2. The standard deviation of the characteristic to be studied.

By substituting these two numbers in the formula, the size of the sample is quickly calculated.

In the study of weekly payrolls in food stores, it may be that a standard error of the mean of $10 will be acceptable. In other words, if the average of the sample differs from the real average of the population *by no more than this amount,* the study will be a success.

The statistician has also found out that the standard deviation (σ) of the weekly payrolls is about $100. He then uses the formula to determine the necessary sample size.

$$\sigma_{\bar{x}} = \frac{\sigma}{\sqrt{n}} \quad \text{or} \quad 10 = \frac{100}{\sqrt{n}}$$

$$10\sqrt{n} = 100 \quad \text{or} \quad \sqrt{n} = \frac{100}{10} = 10$$

(By squaring both sides of the equation—multiplying each side by itself—the square root sign is eliminated.)

$$\sqrt{n} = 10 \quad \text{or} \quad n = 100$$

It can now be said: If the standard deviation of weekly payrolls is $100, a sample of 100 stores is needed to obtain a standard error of the mean of $10. The mean of the weekly payrolls as a result of this sample will not differ from the mean of the population by more than about $10.

One question may puzzle you. How is it possible to know the standard deviation of a characteristic if we are now deciding a sample size to study it? This is a problem for the statistician, too. Here are some ways of solving it:

1. A study like this one may have been done in the past. Perhaps this characteristic does not change very quickly.

2. From the results of an entirely different type of study, it may be possible to estimate a standard deviation. For example, another study may show the number of workers in food stores, rather than payrolls. Under certain conditions, the weekly payrolls could be figured out.

3. If there is no information at all, a small study of a few food stores may be made. This is called a *pilot study.* Its only purpose is to obtain some information in advance of the larger study. One item would be the possible size of the standard deviation.

A discussion of confidence levels, or confidence limits, has purposely been omitted. In a real study, it would play an important part in deciding sample size. Deciding confidence limits requires the use of special tables beyond the scope of this book. It may be noted that at a 95 percent level of confidence, the size of the sample of food stores would jump from 100 to 385 stores. With such a sample, it could be said: There are 95 chances out of 100 that the true mean (average) of the population would fall between the average payroll shown by the sample, plus or minus the standard error of the mean ($10).

For a 99 percent level of confidence (99 chances out of 100), the sample would increase to 666 stores.

The cost of increased confidence is a larger sample.

It should be clear by now that a statistician does a great deal of investigating and makes many decisions long before any study begins.

Other Samples

Systematic sampling

Random probability sampling is the basis of all sampling. Even when it is not followed in its purest form, it serves as a model. The temptation is often great to avoid the true random sample. Usually, the cost of doing a statistical study is behind this. It may be that the sampling frame is very large, possibly over 100,000 cards. The cards have not been numbered. What may be done is to choose only the first card by random digits. Then, every hundredth card is picked for the sample. If the first random digit is 8, cards 108, 208, 308, etc., are used.

This is called *systematic sampling.* The fate of all the items in the population depends upon the first random digit.

Cluster Sampling

In a purely random sample, odd situations often arise. One store or person may be a hundred miles away from the next nearest one. If personal visits have to be made, this is a very expensive visit. In order to avoid this possibility, an area (state, city, block) may be divided into sections, much like the flower bed. A random sample of sections is then selected. Everyone in these sections is in the sample.

This is known as *cluster sampling*. A cluster is a bunch, and sampling things in bunches is cheaper.

Stratified sampling

One type of sampling deserves special attention. Under certain conditions it can result in a smaller "error" than the simple random sample. It is called *stratified sampling*. "Stratum" in Latin means "layer." The plural is "strata." It doesn't sound as tempting, but a layer cake could be called a stratified cake.

The strata are groupings of the population. Male and female is a common separation into groups. Age groups often form strata. The groupings must have some meaning for the purpose of the study. They do if the scatter (or variability) of the characteristic is different stratum by stratum, or from group to group.

Imagine that instead of studying the total payroll in food stores, we were interested in the wages of individual workers. Stores with one worker would probably have very little scatter. The worker in such a store is most likely to be a sales or stock clerk, a delivery boy or an all-around helper. Such workers do not usually earn much. Even if all one-worker food stores in a city were in one group, there would be very little mixture.

But consider large supermarkets with one hundred workers or more. These would have, in addition to the above, a manager, an assistant manager, managers of the fruit and vegetable section and the meat department, butchers and their assistants, perhaps a bookkeeper, a timekeeper, a truck driver, and others. Among these are high-paid as well as low-paid workers. The scatter is great.

When sensible groupings exist in a large population, a stratified sample is desirable. Each stratum then becomes a population of its own. From each stratum, or sub-population, a random sample is then chosen. The proportionate size of the sample may be different in each stratum. Where the scatter is greatest, as in the very large stores, the sample may include every other store. Where the scatter is likely to be smallest, as in stores with one or two workers, the sample may include only every twentieth store.

The stratified sample could be a "layer cake" as shown below.

When the division into strata makes sense, the standard error of the mean of all the stores in the sample will be smaller than if a simple random sample had been chosen.

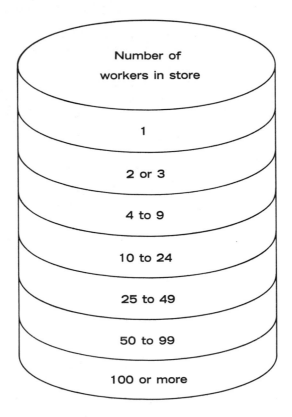

Number of
workers in store

1

2 or 3

4 to 9

10 to 24

25 to 49

50 to 99

100 or more

Sequential sampling

Having just completed layer cakes, it may not be appetizing to go back to meat pies. Meat pies are "destroyed" in testing as well as in eating. In such sampling, the sooner a decision is reached, the lower the cost.

The interest here is not directly in a measure such as the mean or the standard error of the mean. Such measures may have to be calculated. But the main interest is in *making a decision.* The decision may be: good or bad, accept or reject. When this answer cannot be given, the decision may be: continue to sample.

Such sampling often tests manufactured articles or work done. The aim is to avoid two possible mistakes:

1. Accepting something bad or undesirable.
2. Rejecting something good or desirable.

Either of these mistakes involves a loss of time or money.

Sequential sampling is used when things must be destroyed. To choose *in sequence* means to choose one after another, in some order, not all at once.

An interesting fact about sequential sampling is that it is almost never done by a statistician. The statistician only designs a *sampling plan.* This may be in the form of charts, graphs, or tables. The inspector or other user then follows the plan. From the plan, he makes his decision.

In the meat pie example, the plan may tell him:

1. The smallest number of pies from any machine to choose for his sample.
2. The way to select his sample of cartons and which pie in the carton to test.
3. After testing, consult the chart on the next page.

If the number of "good" or "bad" doesn't match the chart, the sampling is continued. For example, an inspector has tested 10 pies; 2 were below standard. He would continue to sample. Naturally, he cannot continue sampling forever. The plan would tell him how and when to reach a decision if he goes beyond the numbers on the table.

Number of pies sampled	Good lots: Accept if the number below standard is not more than	Bad lots: Reject if the number below standard is at least
5	0	2
6	0	2
7	0	2
8	0	3
9	1	3
10	1	3
etc.	etc.	etc.

If the company inspects its own pies, it will do it in some other way. It will certainly do its sampling before the pies are in the cartons. Its standards will be different. A company's testing of its own product is called *quality control.*

Each meat pie, it was said, is supposed to contain at least two ounces of meat. A government inspector is only interested in this minimum. If the pie contains five ounces of meat, it is a satisfactory pie to him.

But the company wants to produce a pie with *exactly* two ounces of meat. A pie with more than that means a loss of money. Its own sampling plan will be designed to control two things:

1. That there are no pies with less than two ounces of meat. By doing this, it will satisfy its customers, have no rejected orders, and avoid trouble with government inspectors.

2. That the machines making the pies have not gone "wild"; that they are not overloading the pies with meat. This test is a check on the production process (the making) itself. It is a check on the machines.

The control of quality and the production process by statistical methods came into use during World War II. At that time, there was a tremendous increase in production, mainly for the war. Products rolled off machines in great quantity, and they had to be of uniform quality. Many rejects would have hurt the war effort. The method of statistical quality control played an important part in keeping down the number of poor products. One man who played an important part in developing it is Walter A. Shewhart of the Bell Telephone Laboratories. Quality control is today part of every process in which things are produced in large number.

Public opinion polls

Public opinion polls are by far the most popular and familiar uses of sampling. They are used to estimate which are the most popular television programs; how people feel about important affairs; how people will vote in an election. If you read a newspaper, especially at election time, you may be aware of polls. Your parents may have discussed them. Your social studies class may have debated their use or results. The number of polls increases steadily. Exactly what are they?

A poll is a sample of opinion. At election time, it is like a mock or imitation election. However, only a selected sample votes. From this sample, the pollster (the man or group taking the poll) tries to estimate the probable results of the real election to come. Many polls are taken privately for candidates who are willing to pay for them.

The poll is, in its way, an answer to normal human curiosity. For many, it answers the question, "Where do we stand?" or, "Who is likely to win?" The results of polls are published in magazines and newspapers, which pay for their use.

An election poll may appear in a newspaper as follows:

Question: *For which candidate do you intend to vote in the coming election?*

Candidate	Percent of voters
A (*Democrat*)	45
B (*Republican*)	44
C (*other party*)	1
Undecided	10
	100

It is not unusual for the "undecided" votes to be left out altogether. These votes are divided among the major parties by the pollster.

Such polls, even for a national election, seldom include a sample of more than 3,000 people. This would be enough if the sample were of the random probability type, but very few are. Often, the choosing of the sample is no more scientific than that done by the youngsters at the flower bed.

The published results of polls almost never tell the type of sample used. The size of the sample is also often a mystery. The standard error of the mean — in these cases, the percent of voters favoring a candidate — is never shown. And this writer has never seen the confidence limits of any poll.

Since the failure of the *Literary Digest* poll, there has been none to equal it. But, in 1948, most polls showed Thomas E. Dewey leading President Harry Truman by a very comfortable margin. Of course, President Truman carried the election.

Presidential elections are often close. The late President Kennedy's margin of victory over Richard Nixon in 1960 was less than 1 percent. A difference of only 3 or 4 percent between candidates is not unusual. It is clear that the standard error of the percent can easily be greater than this even in a random sample. Therefore, a poll may show that a candidate will receive 52 percent of the vote. Taking into account the standard error of this percent, in the actual election he may receive 48 percent or 56 percent. This is assuming a standard error of 4 percent (52 plus or minus an "error" of 4 percent). It can make the difference between losing an election and running away with it.

The largest error of polls does not arise from the "error" of sampling. Other errors pile up. No one knows, for example, how the "undecided" persons will vote. Are Republicans more "undecided" than Democrats? This can only be estimated *after* a particular election. Also, a man may vote one way in a poll and change his mind on Election Day. Are Democrats more likely than Republicans to change their minds?

Another important factor is that many Americans do not bother to vote. Anyone in the sample can vote in the poll; the poll comes to the possible voter. But even in Presidential elections, it is not rare for more than 25 percent of eligible voters (1 out of 4) not to vote at all. In a close election, those who stay home may be deciding the election. Who are they?

A poll also influences its own results. Here is how this can happen.

A leading poll shows that candidate A will probably receive 53 percent of the vote. Mr. Smith reads this. He is for candidate A. But since he now feels that candidate A will win without his vote, he stays home to paint his basement. He doesn't vote.

Mr. Brown also reads the results of the poll. He is for candidate B. He had intended to stay home to paint his basement since he felt sure that *his* candidate would win. The poll changes his mind. Instead of painting his basement, he votes.

In this way, the poll itself helps to prove itself wrong.

Whatever one may think of them, polls are playing a more and more important part in American life. The following stories from *The New York Times* make this clear.

The first story appeared in the paper on July 6, 1964, under the headline, "Humphrey Leads Poll for 2nd Spot":

A confidential poll that found Senator Hubert H. Humphrey of Minnesota to be the best Democratic Vice-Presidential running mate for President Johnson has excited the interest of the White House.

The poll . . . was based on a national cross-section sample of 1,600 possible voters, a normal probability poll sample.

This poll was taken during May, 1964.

About six weeks after the story appeared, President Johnson chose Senator Humphrey as his running-mate.

A more interesting story appeared on August 27, 1964, after the President had made his choice. It discussed how he had made up his mind. The above poll is mentioned as one that influenced him.

Here are quotations from that story:

In May, Louis Bean was commissioned, most likely by a White House aide, to take a public opinion poll. . . . Mr. Bean took a nationwide survey . . . and found Mr. Humphrey leading Mr. Kennedy by about two points.

The pollster went to the White House . . . and . . . the President called Mr. Humphrey to report the news. . . .

For months before his choice was finally announced, Mr. Johnson conducted one of his most searching interrogations of his party and its leaders in modern times. His instruments were polls, telephone calls, personal conversations, conferences. . . .

Mr. Johnson placed considerable reliance on the various polls taken for him.

Other polls that the President had taken for him are also mentioned.

Senator Humphrey, too, ordered polls taken for him. He showed the results to the President.

It is plain that public opinion polls played a very important part in the choice of a Vice-Presidential candidate in 1964.

In the United States the Vice-President is separated by only one man from the most important office in the country and one of the most powerful in the world. It is not stretching the facts to say that sampling, in the form of polls, plays a part in deciding the fate of nations. This is a tremendous responsibility. It has become more important than ever that polling be done according to the strictest scientific standards.

5 COMPUTERS AND AUTOMATION

HOW FAST is a billionth of a second? Can you imagine one billion calculations being done in one second? This is the speed at which electronic computers will soon be working. If you started to count (not calculate!) right now and did so for 40 hours each week at a rate of 80 numbers each minute, you might be able to count to one billion in a century!

In considering the speed of computers, or "thinking machines," as you may have heard them called, we must deal with the results of counting or of measurement that man cannot "picture" in his mind, such as the speed of light at 186,000 miles per second or the number of stars in the universe. They go beyond our imagination.

No invention in the history of mankind has had such immediate and wide application as the electronic computer. In its short life, it has opened new opportunities for science and mathematics, changed the nature of national defense, changed entire industries, and affected the lives of many people. But these effects are as nothing compared to those that will almost certainly come. Most experts agree that within the next twenty-five or fifty years, at most, the computer will have changed man's way of life—his work, his leisure, his education, even his way of thinking.

In 1949, the author was at the headquarters of the International Business Machines Corporation (IBM) for a training course. The climax of the visit was an introduction to one of the earliest computers. It was not yet called that; its official title was *electronic calculator.*

This introduction was one never to be forgotten. In a large room, one very long wall was entirely covered with vacuum tubes, much like those in nontransistor radios. At one end of the room, on a low glass-covered balcony, was a machine through which a long paper tape was passing. Elsewhere, IBM cards were moving rapidly through other machines. As the tape and cards moved, thousands and thousands of vacuum tubes along the wall flashed on and off, on and off, in what seemed to be a mad dance. The scene was like one from a fantastic space movie before space research became real.

This calculator, we were told, could do 10,000 additions and subtractions in "a few minutes." It could multiply two 14-digit numbers in $\frac{1}{50}$ of a second. A group of commands on a line of the paper tape reached the calculator at the rate of 50 per second. Compared with those of today's computer, these speeds are slower than those of a horse and buggy compared with the fastest supersonic jet!

In 1964, only fifteen years later, the author was again at IBM to study the modern computer. The wonder was no longer in its appearance; it looked like a colorful refrigerator. The wonder was in what the computer could do. A millionth of a second to add two 48-digit numbers! This was what the mind now had to grasp.

The purpose of this chapter is not to make you sit up and wonder. True, there is cause for wonder. But the computer is made by men and women for man's use. It will undoubtedly play a part in your adult life. Therefore, it is important to know how the computer grew up; what it does; how it does it; what its future may be.

This is our story.

A Short History of Calculating Machines

In 1671, a famous mathematician, Gottfried Wilhelm von Leibnitz (1646–1716), wrote, "It is unworthy of excellent men to lose hours like slaves in the labor of calculation which could safely be relegated to anyone else if machines were used." This is the basic idea that drives men to develop better calculating machines.

The first calculating "machine" was man's fingers and toes. These are used today not only by children but also by many primitive peoples. The different ways in which they are used is a fascinating story.

The first device to make arithmetic easier was the abacus. No one knows when it was first used. It has been traced back as far as the fifth century B.C. The Chinese are usually given credit for its invention. Today it is still widely used in that country, in India, and in Japan. You can see one in many Chinese laundries in the United States.

The abacus is a frame, or rack, with wires stretched in horizontal rows. Along the wires are movable beads. The beads represent digits; the wires are the "places"—tens, hundreds, etc. An expert with the abacus can add as fast as a man with an electric desk-adding machine.

The slide rule is another mathematical device. It is a stick resembling a ruler with grooves. Along the grooves, other sticks can be moved back and forth. By matching the markings on the sticks, rapid multiplication and division can be done. Several men built slide rules in the early seventeenth century. In 1850, a French army officer, Amédée Mannheim, perfected the modern slide rule. Today, it is widely used by engineers.

The first real arithmetic machine was developed in 1642 by the great mathematician, Blaise Pascal, whose name appears in this book more than once. That was the year of Sir Isaac Newton's birth, but it was not intended as a birthday present for him. Pascal's machine (see illustration on page 204) can be bought today in several forms as a child's toy. Pascal himself was not quite nineteen years old when he built it.

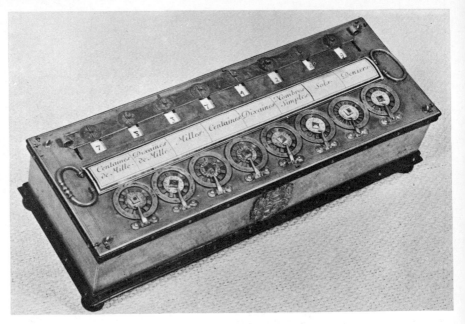

A model of Blaise Pascal's arithmetic calculator developed in 1642. It could compute sums up to the hundred thousands. (IBM)

Pascal's machine was meant to do addition automatically. It didn't work too well, but that was not his fault. The machinists of his day could not make the parts fine enough. This was to be a cause of failure of other men's attempts well into the nineteenth century.

The next attempt at constructing a calculating machine was made by Leibnitz in 1671. His was meant to do multiplication. It suffered the same fate as Pascal's.

The first calculating machine to be produced and sold came a century and a half later. In 1820, Charles X. Thomas, an inventor, built a machine that could add, subtract, multiply, and divide. Many men in many countries improved upon his machine in later years.

At about this time, in England, there came upon the scene a strange mathematical genius. Charles Babbage (1792–1871) was interested in many things. He was mainly responsible for the introduction of uniform postage rates for letters mailed anywhere within a country.

Babbage had built what in his time was called a *difference engine*. The machine's function was to solve simple equations, such as $X^2 + X + 19$, for values of X. In 1833, he conceived the idea of building an *analytical machine* (see illustration below). This would, if successful, solve *any* mathematical problem at a

A model of Charles Babbage's Analytical Engine. He intended to use it to calculate the values for certain standard mathematical tables. (IBM; *photograph by Geoffrey Clements*)

rate of 60 additions per minute. Remember, this was before the use of electricity!

Charles Babbage was not an idle dreamer. The British government was willing to finance most of his work. The rest of Babbage's life was spent on his machine, which was never completed. Again, the technology of his day was far behind his ideas.

He is called by many people the father of the modern computer. His "analytical machine" was designed to have a "store" to keep information until needed. This resembles the "memory" of the computer, as we shall see. It was to have a "mill" (the word for factory then) where the mathematical work would be done. This is like another part of the modern computer. A transfer device was to carry information from "store" to "mill" and back. Babbage even designed a punch card on which to enter information.

Babbage died in 1871 a disappointed man, still far ahead of his time.

In the middle of the nineteenth century, two important types of machines were developed. They were the desk calculator and adding machine, with a paper tape. Today, electrically driven sleek models can be seen in almost any office or bank. Your school may have one or both. The cash register developed from these machines.

Herman Hollerith, a U.S. census employee, was responsible for the next giant stride forward. In 1889, he designed the familiar punch card, shown early in this book (page 10). He also developed an electric machine that could count the cards and add numbers punched into them. Hollerith cards and machines were used to tally the results of the 1890 census. They were used in many countries well into the twentieth century.

From this machine, the development of the electronic calculators and accounting machines, and then computers, was inevitable. Great companies came into the field. Their research, especially at IBM and Remington Rand, continued to turn out new and improved models constantly. The tabulators and accounting machines perform a wide variety of mathematical operations at high speed, although far below that of computers. In 1964, they were still far more common than computers.

As is often the case with invention, while this was going on, men were experimenting with advanced machinery, the basic models of today's electronic computers. One such man was Dr. Vannevar Bush, a great name in American science. In 1925, working with others at the Massachusetts Institute of Technology, he built an analog calculator. ("Analog" is a word we shall soon discuss.) This machine measured angles by turns of gears, electrically operated.

In 1942, a new model could measure angles electronically. The word "electronic" had come to stay. By today's standards, the speed of the machine was modest. What a man could do in two weeks the machine could do in one hour. It was put to work revising the U.S. Army's artillery firing tables.

With the end of World War II in sight, developments came with breakneck speed. Famous names fly across the pages. It is only possible to present the highlights.

In 1944, IBM perfected a machine (the Automatic Sequence Controlled Calculator) that functioned on the principles of a computer. This was followed by the machine the author saw and described, called the Selective Sequence Electronic Calculator. In 1945, two great engineers, J. Presper Eckert and John Mauchly, built a machine called ENIAC. This was another "first" in the series of electronic calculators.

Two sets of events now took place. Mathematical geniuses contributed theory, or ideas. Great engineers contributed technology, or "know-how," an ability to make things. The paths crisscross or proceed side by side. Dr. John von Neumann, one of the greatest mathematicians of this century, wrote a paper on "The General and Logical Theory of Automata." ("Automata" means self-operating machines.) In it, he outlined the basic ideas of computer design. Norbert Wiener (1894–1964), a pioneer American mathematician who made many contribu-

A section of the vacuum tubes in the arithmetical unit of the Selective Sequence Electronic Calculator, a 1948 model of present-day computers. (IBM)

tions to his field, coined the term "cybernetics" to describe self-governing devices that feed back information to govern themselves. Dr. Herman H. Goldstine, who was later to become Director of Mathematical Research at IBM, together with his associate, Dr. Arthur W. Burks, and Dr. von Neumann, worked out the method of using binary numbers (we'll soon get to them) in computers.

With the birth of the transistor—an amplifier of electrical power much smaller in size than the vacuum tube it replaced—in 1948 and the magnetic core—tiny rings of magnetized material—in 1950, the basis was established for the modern computer.

In 1951, UNIVAC I, the first of the truly modern computers, built by Eckert and Mauchly for Sperry Rand Corporation, was delivered to the U.S. Bureau of the Census. A sign of progress in this field: in 1963, at the age of twelve, the machine became an old museum piece. In that year, it was sent to the Smithsonian Institution in Washington, D.C., to join the Wright brothers' airplane and Bell's telephone.

What Computers Do

At the end of 1964, there were about 18,000 computers in use in the United States. More than 1,600 were with the federal government, about one-third in the Air Force. Among private users, the Bell Telephone system and the General Electric Company led the list, the former with more than 400, the latter with more than 200.

The cost of most computers is between $100,000 and $3,000,000. Special computers for the Atomic Energy Commission, NASA (the space agency), and others may cost more than $7,000,000. A complete system (called Sabre) such as IBM installed for American Airlines may cost as much as $30,000,-000.

The value of all computers in the United States in 1964 was over $5,000,000,000. With extra equipment that usually goes with them, not counting the special air-conditioning that computers need, the value of all computer setups was about $10,000,000,000.

What do they do for all this money?

Most computers do ordinary work—but in an extraordinary way. They make out and address bills for practically anything.

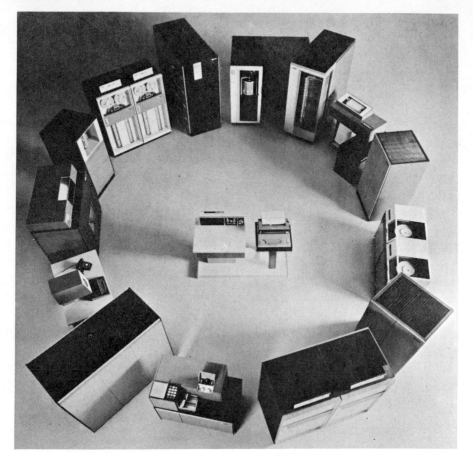

A complete modern computer set-up, IBM's System 360. In the center is a console unit that permits direct access to the computer. Thus, programed instructions may be modified without halting the operation. (IBM)

Look at your telephone bill or one from a large department store. A computer probably did everything but deliver it to your door. When your parents make a payment, the computer will give them credit for it; any balance due (an unpaid amount) will be shown on the next bill. If your parents pay by check, the computer may sort the checks when they reach the bank.

Since all of this takes so little of the computer's time, it will also make out a payroll. Today's payrolls have become very complicated. Below are some of the steps from a real payroll.

A man earns $120 per week for working 40 hours, we will assume. If he works more than 40 hours, he receives $4.50 per hour, or 1½ times his regular hourly rate of pay. The computer calculates his *gross* pay, based upon his hours of work. This is his pay before deductions, of which there are many in today's world. Here are *some* types of deductions from one paycheck:

Type of deduction	*How it is calculated*
Life insurance	This is a fixed weekly amount
Union dues	This is a fixed weekly amount
Health insurance	This is a fixed weekly amount
Retirement plan	This is a percent of gross pay
Federal income tax	This is a percent of gross pay
State income tax	This is a percent of gross pay
Unemployment insurance	This is a percent of gross pay
U.S. Savings Bonds	This is a fixed weekly amount—but the computer must signal when a bond is due and for how much
Personal loans	This is a fixed weekly amount—but the computer must signal a paid-up loan
Social Security	This is a percent of gross pay—but there is a maximum. The computer must deduct only enough. The last payment may be smaller than all others

After making these calculations, the computer subtracts the total from the gross pay. It then prints out for each worker a list of his deductions, each amount, and a paycheck—if anything is left.

Payroll-making, even for the largest company in the United States, does not take up all the rest of the computer's time. It must be given other work. It may keep an inventory—a record of goods coming in and going out. When the goods on hand reach a low point, the computer can write out an order for more. It may help plan a sales campaign. It prepares up-to-the-minute reports of the company's profit or loss. It may pick a sample for a company survey. It will certainly tabulate the statistical results.

It takes an enormous amount of work to keep a computer busy. And due to its high cost, it cannot be allowed to stand idle to decorate the place.

These are a few of the ordinary uses of computers. But this statement was made earlier: "No invention in the history of mankind has had such immediate and wide application."

In reading what follows, keep this in mind: The first computer was delivered in 1951. In 1964, the electronic computer had just entered its "teens."

Many volumes would be needed to describe all the uses to which computers are put. There is probably no one man qualified to write such an encyclopedia. Books about computers now number in the thousands. There are many magazines that deal only with this subject. Other magazines regularly have articles about them.

One or two uses from several fields are listed below. They will give you a taste of the enormously wide range of use. The examples are neither the most nor least important, neither the most nor least complicated. They are merely examples.

Defense

The entire American air defense and attack system, should either ever be necessary through an undesirable event, is built around computers. The system is called SAGE and is operated by the U.S. Air Force. *Every* plane above the earth in the United States and Canada is identified by radar. The information, friend or foe, type of plane, speed, its location at every instant, a description of the location (mountains, open fields, etc.), is automatically fed into computers. The same would be true of rockets or missiles. In the event of enemy attack, computers would alert Air Force planes, assign their targets, and send out interceptor missiles and rockets.

It is obvious that with the speed of modern jets and rockets, only the speed of computers could give timely warning.

At this point, it should be emphasized that every large industrial country produces computers. Their defense and attack systems are probably designed along the same lines.

Space

John Glenn and all other astronauts "flew" by computer. Their orbits, their positions, and their bodily reactions were automatically relayed to computers. Their time and place of re-entry into the earth's atmosphere were determined by computers.

A battery of computers calculates the position of Telstar, the communications satellite. You can see a Telstar tracking station in action if you visit Andover, Maine.

All satellites are controlled by computer and send back their information to computers.

Billions of calculations are already being made on computers about the problems of sending a manned ship to the moon. Some of these deal with the probable position of meteorites on several target dates for this expedition.

Education

When a city-wide, state-wide, or national test is given, all the papers can be marked by a computer in less time than it takes a student to finish the test.

A computer planned the construction of a college building. It also showed how to plan the college's program to use the space 80 percent of the time; 50 percent is about the usual amount of use. This resulted in a saving of several million dollars for the school.

Science

An article in *Scientific American* magazine reported that an IBM STRETCH computer (a special model) was used at Los

Alamos Scientific Laboratory to aid in certain chemical experiments. To solve the complex problem, the computer had to solve the Newtonian equations of motion 150 million times.

Translation

Computers translate languages. Below is a sample of translation from the Chinese.

現在的導彈巳能帶上原子彈和氫彈的彈頭，因而宅是一種破壞力很大的兵器．

MODERN GUIDED-MISSILE ALREADY POSSIBLE CARRY WITH WAR HEAD OF HYDROGEN BOMB AND ATOMIC BOMB, THEREFORE IT IS ONE KIND WEAPON WITH VERY BIG POWER OF DESTRUCTION.

Sample translation of Chinese shows the present state of the machine-translation art. It was produced by methods devised by International Business Machines Corporation.

Industry

In oil refining, chemical, paper, and cement making, instruments measure such things as temperature, pressure, flow, etc. These measurements go directly into a computer. If one of these factors or a combination is wrong, the computer corrects it.

Fun and games

You cannot beat a computer at ticktacktoe. You cannot beat it in a game of checkers. You may beat it at chess, if you are a whiz.

Simulation

Computers can *simulate*. This is playing a game of make-believe. It is done when all the facts are not known or can never be known. First, all possible conditions, or very many of them, are made up; then they can be tested on a computer. This is simulation. The speed of the computer makes it possible to try an endless number of combinations. The ability to do this is important to science, mathematics, and industry.

Baseball

If you are a baseball fan, you may have dreamed of an ideal ball game. Christy Mathewson, Walter Johnson, Ty Cobb, and Babe Ruth would all be in the game. You can name your own teams.

It is possible to feed into a computer the lifetime records of the players in the smallest detail — walked on four pitches by a left-hander with a man on second base with the score tied in the last of the fifth, etc. Once this tremendous mass of detail is in the machine, the "umpire" can call, "Play ball."

The computer would bring each man to bat. Since it can select random digits, you would not know what was coming next — as in a real ball game. As the game moved along, the computer could produce a tape that would give a play-by-play account of the game. At the end, there would be a total of runs, hits, and errors for both sides.

Does this sound "way out"? Such a game has already been played!

Weather

The U.S. Weather Bureau has tried to simulate world-wide weather conditions for long-range forecasting. This problem involved: 10,000 grid points (points on the globe), 9 levels in the atmosphere, time units of 5 minutes (288 per day), and many other factors, called variables. The number of permutations and combinations is fantastically high.

If you have been wondering, "Who ever needs a billion calculations?" this is one example. The number of calculations on an IBM STRETCH computer was high in the billions!

The ability to simulate on a computer has become one of man's most powerful tools. Scientists can study problems of the earth, the stars, the behavior of sub-atomic particles that could never be undertaken before. Mathematicians use it to try to solve unsolved problems. The U.S. Air Force has simulated great air battles and changed tactics, depending upon the results.

Information retrieval

Another important operation of the computer is *retrieval.* "Retrieval" means "bringing back." From an enormous mass of information placed into its "memory," a computer can bring back, or retrieve, exactly what is wanted.

Science

In science, there is today an "information explosion." Thousands of articles, books, and speeches are published monthly. Many are translations from foreign publications. Most scientists want to know what is going on in their field. They may also want some special information. However, it is becoming more difficult to keep up with what is written.

One solution, which many universities are using, is to put the articles into a computer. Either the entire article may be placed in the computer, or it may be indexed by means of a code, as in some libraries. At the scientist's request, the computer can retrieve exactly what he wants. It may be, for example, everything that has been written about the relationship between cigarette smoking and cancer. The retrieval may be in the form of a copy of the article.

Law

The University of Pennsylvania has placed into a computer, by means of magnetic tape, *all* the laws of Pennsylvania, New York, New Jersey, and the regulations of the Bureau of Internal Revenue (income tax). If a lawyer should want to know all references to "Rights of Minors," for example, the computer can immediately give him a list of books, legal cases, page numbers, and so forth.

In many universities the professors are going back to class —but not to teach. Gray-haired presidents of large corporations and important government officials are taking time off— but not for vacations. Where are they going? They are headed for training classes in the use of computers. Some of these classes are conducted by the universities, others by computer manufacturers such as IBM.

Most of these people will never themselves operate a computer, but professors cannot organize research, company officers cannot run their business efficiently, government officials cannot manage an agency, unless they know what a computer can do. This is a fact of modern life.

How a Computer Does Its Work

Far back in his history, man sharpened a stone. With it, he could more easily kill animals, for his safety or his food. Later, he invented a simple plow. When pulled by an animal, the plow could dig deeper furrows for man to plant his seed. With these tools, he expanded his muscle power. Most machines invented since then have done just this—they enlarged man's muscle. Today, he presses a button and, in one movement, a huge machine stamps out the wing of an airplane.

The computer is a new type of tool. It enlarges man's brain. Man knows much less about his brain than about his muscle. This may be a reason why some men fear the computer, as if it might replace man. Some call it a "thinking machine." They speak with wonder and amazement of its "memory." They make it seem a magic device.

The computer is a machine for man's use. It can do little things for itself, but under man's control. Man tells it what to do and, mainly, exactly how to do it. It will help your understanding of it if you think of a computer as a machine and not a mystery.

Analog computers

The family of computers has two main branches: analog and digital. The analog computer is much less popular. It will be described briefly.

"Analog" comes from the word "analogy." We say of someone, "He's as sly as a fox," when we mean that he is tricky. Or, "He's as strong as an ox." We are comparing by analogy; we are not establishing an exact likeness.

Many common instruments work by analogy. A good example is the altimeter of an airplane. It measures the plane's elevation (height above the earth) by pressure on the instrument. It doesn't measure the height directly, as would a tape measure; it makes an analogy between pressure and height in feet.

An analog computer works in the same way. It compares physical quantities or amounts. The physical quantity may be a weight, the number of degrees that a wheel turns, or a measure of length.

First, a standard is set with which to make the analogy. Let us say that the standard is a 12-inch ruler. If we then measure a yardstick, it will register as "3" because a yardstick is 3 times as long as a 12-inch ruler, which is the standard. The comparing and measuring are done in one operation, instantly, and with the great speed of computers.

The accuracy of an analog computer is not as great as that of a digital, but it is very great by other standards. In most cases, its accuracy is not *absolute* but *relative*. When a digital computer adds to a million, we can be sure that it is *exactly* a million; its accuracy is absolute. When an analog computer makes a measurement of a million, it is probably *very close* to that—but not exactly a million.

The analog computer has no memory; it is used where this function of the computer is not necessary. It is often used for work or scientific experiments where it is important to know what is going on *as it is happening.* Someone at a control panel filled with switches can watch and make changes as the work is going on.

Many operations in industry are controlled by analog computers. They are used to control artillery firing. They are also used in wind-tunnel experiments to test the effects of high speeds on human beings, or the strength of materials in rockets. In all these, memory is not important. The speed of the computer and the ability to control and change the conditions of an experiment are important.

Digital computers

The digital computer can only add, subtract, multiply, divide, and compare. It may startle you to realize that it does all the amazing things mentioned earlier with these small abilities. But anything that can be changed into a number can be handled by a digital computer.

Most things can be changed into number form. For example, there is a code — a standard set of numbers — for every letter of the alphabet. The places on a chessboard can be coded in numbers; so can the chess pieces. Once this is done, a computer can play chess.

Mathematical equations, no matter how complicated, are finally a set of additions, subtractions, or a combination of simple arithmetic steps. The number of steps may be in the millions, but a million calculations are a second's work to some computers.

In addition to speed of calculation, the computer introduced a new dimension in accuracy. Here is what John von Neumann, the "father" of the logical design of computers, said about this: "They [computing machines] not only have to perform a billion or more steps in a short time, but in a considerable part of the procedure . . . they are permitted not a single error."

Dr. von Neumann pointed out that millions of steps may also be involved in the working of other machines. Television transmission or radar or a microphone may have a "signal" bouncing back and forth millions of times. These may lead to a picture, an image, or a sound. If some of these steps are imperfect (or "wrong"), the final result may still be satisfactory. A perfect result is not the only acceptable one.

In a computer, however, the steps are linked. A mistake anywhere along the way means that the answer is wrong. Its accuracy cannot be approximate; it must be exact. Nothing else has to function with such a degree of accuracy.

One reason for the computer's extraordinary accuracy is that it does its arithmetic in a way that is different from ours. Let's examine its secrets.

The Binary System of Numeration

Early computers used the decimal system, as you and I do. Since this system is *based upon 10,* the highest single digit is 1 less than 10, or 9. The digits run from 0 to 9. In any numeration system, the highest single digit is *1 less than the base.* In a system based upon 8 (it exists), the highest digit is 7.

It was found that the decimal numerals — 0 to 9 — slowed up the computer. In theory, it was known that a system based upon two numbers only would be best. In this system, 0 and 1 are the only digits. It is called the *binary system of numeration.*

The binary system is faster and more logical than a base-ten system. An electric switch is binary in nature. It is either on or off, open or closed. An electrical impulse or a magnetized point is either present or absent. A space on a punch card is either punched or not punched. Points are either electrically charged or not. All these conditions of "either-or" can be coded 0 or 1.

Today's computers use the binary system of numeration. Let's forget old habits, for a while, at least, and learn some simple binary.

Binary digits are shown as if they were holes in punch cards. Start at the right with the decimal value of 1 *when the spot is filled in,* or punched. The value of each spot doubles as we move to the left. Each spot stands for the decimal value as shown. Remember, the computer only asks whether or not the hole is punched. It doesn't care what value *we* assign to the hole or spot.

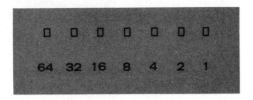

In normal computer use, only the four spaces on the right (8, 4, 2, 1) are used. With them, any decimal digit can be written. See page 222.

In the decimal system we do not write, 0001; we write 1. The zeros to the left of the last real digit are meaningless. They are in binary, too. We write ▐ for 1. For 4, we show ▐ ⬜ ⬜. The empty boxes to the left are dropped when we write numerals in the binary system of numeration.

Other arithmetic operations are a little more complicated. If you are curious, there are some examples in the Answer Section. The important thing to know is how a computer does its arithmetic and why it does it that way.

Talking the Language of Computers

Since Sputnik I, the field of rocketry has created a language all its own. Today, "countdown" is probably as widely under-

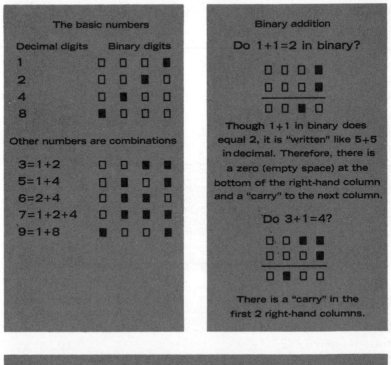

The basic numbers

Decimal digits	Binary digits
1	□ □ □ ■
2	□ □ ■ □
4	□ ■ □ □
8	■ □ □ □

Other numbers are combinations

3=1+2	□ □ ■ ■
5=1+4	□ ■ □ ■
6=2+4	□ ■ ■ □
7=1+2+4	□ ■ ■ ■
9=1+8	■ □ □ ■

Binary addition

Do 1+1=2 in binary?

□ □ □ ■
□ □ □ ■
———
□ □ ■ □

Though 1+1 in binary does equal 2, it is "written" like 5+5 in decimal. Therefore, there is a zero (empty space) at the bottom of the right-hand column and a "carry" to the next column.

Do 3+1=4?

□ □ ■ ■
□ □ □ ■
———
□ ■ □ □

There is a "carry" in the first 2 right-hand columns.

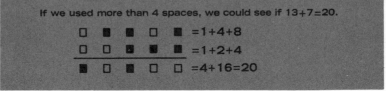

If we used more than 4 spaces, we could see if 13+7=20.

□ ■ ■ □ ■ =1+4+8
□ □ ■ ■ ■ =1+2+4
■ □ ■ □ □ =4+16=20

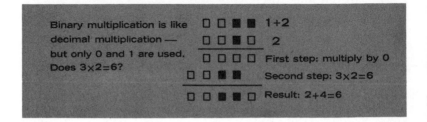

Binary multiplication is like decimal multiplication — but only 0 and 1 are used. Does 3×2=6?

□ □ ■ ■ 1+2
□ □ ■ □ 2
———
□ □ □ □ First step: multiply by 0
□ □ ■ ■ Second step: 3×2=6
———
□ □ ■ ■ □ Result: 2+4=6

stood as "ice-cream soda." The computer, too, has created a new vocabulary. Some familiar words are used in an unfamiliar way. Others are completely new. Below are some of the most common or most important. Let us learn to "talk computer."

Bit: This is a contraction of *Binary Digit*. A "bit" is the smallest possible unit of computer information. One position, or box, of those shown in binary numbers — ▮ — is a bit. Four bits are the equivalent of one decimal digit.

HOW A BINARY BIT LOOKS IN STORAGE

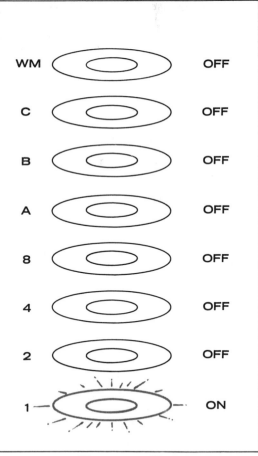

Each doughnut-shaped hole, called a core, has four wires passing through that store information. A core may be "on" or "off." Here, only the 1 position is "on." The computer would read this. The digits are binary values. A and B indicate zones on a punch card; C is used to check digits that are "on"; WM stands for Word Mark. This indicates a break or separation in the information. (IBM)

Storage position

Word: A group of bits handled as one unit in the computer. In early computers, it was fixed: 10 bits = 1 word. Today a word can vary in length or number of bits.

Millisecond: One-thousandth of a second. This is almost an old-fashioned word in computer language.

Microsecond: One-millionth of a second. A present-day word.

Nanosecond: One-billionth of a second. A word with hope in it.

Memory: This is part of the computer itself. In technical language, the memory is a large series of magnetic cores or holes or places. These are usually reached by transistors. The memory is often called "core storage." Into the memory are deposited the instructions for an operation, data (the information), or reference tables (such as square roots). These are "called upon" when needed.

The memory can be enlarged by storing information on magnetic tape or metal disks, which can also be "called upon" when needed.

A new IBM 360 computer provides storage for as many as 8 million characters — the smallest unit of meaningful information — each of which can be available for use in 8/millionths of a second.

Address: Every part of the memory, or core storage, has an address. This is the exact place where instructions or information can be found. To make a computer use its memory, you must give it an address — tell it where to go.

Random access: Imagine that you want the ace of spades from a mixed deck of cards. You can find it by looking at one card after another. This is the serial, or sequence, way. If you were able to reach into the deck and pull it out directly, not by chance, this would be random access. It is the ability of the computer to reach into its memory for any wanted item

Real time: As something is going on, the information about it is available. A correction can be made without interrupting the experiment or waiting for the final result.

A rocket has been fired to achieve a predetermined orbit. It sends back to ground-based computers a continuous stream of information about temperature, radiation, etc. It was decided before firing that if radiation exceeded a certain level, a change in orbit would be made. As the ground-based computer records a sudden sharp change in the radiation level, it automatically signals, by means of a connected radio transmitter, a change in orbit. Such a maneuver is made in *real time*.

Algorithm: This refers to a computer problem that can be clearly stated and that will reach an expected result. Simple examples are making out a bill or a payroll. Such problems are *algorithmic*.

Heuristic: This refers to a computer problem that is not clearly defined. It may not be possible to define it. There may be too many unknown elements. We may also want the computer to handle unexpected elements or examine probabilities. The computer may use trial and error or "learn" by experience. The computer's solution to a problem may be unexpected.

Programing: A program is a set of steps, or operations, in the form of instructions, that is put into the computer. It will carry them out to solve a problem. The instructions must be given in very great detail. You cannot leave it to the computer to figure out what you want. The program is usually fed into the computer in the form of punch cards.

Feedback: This is one of the most important words in computer language. If you live in a private home, you may see feedback in action. It is the relationship between your furnace, the thermostat (like a thermometer), and the heat in the house. The thermostat, connected to the furnace and placed in a room of the house, is set at a desired temperature—let us say 70 degrees. The furnace heats the house. The temperature rises. When it goes above 70 degrees, the thermostat reduces the furnace's heat. The house then cools to below 70 degrees. The thermostat then turns on the furnace. In this way, the temperature of the house is kept at a nearly constant 70 degrees. It is a self-controlled system. This is feedback.

In computers, too, feedback is the ability of the system to be self-correcting or self-adjusting. The computer adjusts a process depending upon whether the results are "good" or "bad." It becomes self-controlled.

In a perfect system of feedback (which does not yet exist), a master computer could control other computers that controlled other machines. No human assistance would be needed. Only the information that came into it would guide the computer.

We are ready now to examine the computer setup itself.

A Computer and Its Assistants

Below is a photograph of an IBM 1401 computer installation.

The 1401, a "workhorse" among computers, was probably

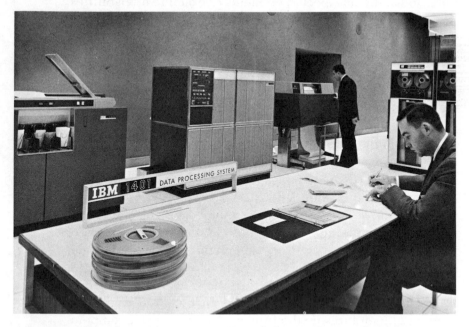

A basic small-scale computer set-up. From left to right: punch card reader, processor, printer, magnetic tape reader. On the table are reels of magnetic tape. (IBM)

the most popular one until the mid-1960's. In 1964–1965, IBM, as well as RCA, Honeywell, General Electric, and other computer manufacturers, came out with what they called "a new generation" of computers. These were more flexible and faster, and could be adapted to a greater variety of tasks. It is probable that by the late 1960's IBM's 360 may replace the 1401, as it is called, in popularity. The 1401 stands about midway in the family of computers, neither fastest nor slowest. The units shown here commonly go together.

Any computer setup must consist of the following units:

An input device (or machine)

Through this unit, instructions and data (information) are fed into the computer. The actual "agent" may be punch cards or magnetic tape. If punch cards are used, a card-reader can read the entire card (80 columns) at once. If magnetic tape is used, it is scanned (that is, read) by a scanner. The scanner can read, or scan, 60,000 characters per second.

The tape looks like a reel of movie film, one-half an inch wide. Since old information on the tape can be "erased," it is used again and again. Tape holds 800 characters per inch by means of magnetized spots on it.

The central processing unit

This is the unit that is meant when we merely say "computer." It is the heart and "brain" of the setup. It contains:
1. A memory, or storage unit.
2. The logic unit.
3. The arithmetic unit.
4. The control unit. This guides the steps. It's like a monitor; it tells the information where to go.

An output device

This prepares a record of the results of the computer's work. The results can be punched into cards, but magnetic tape is most often used.

A printer

This is not really part of the computer setup, but it is very often added. It prints the results on paper, in many forms. Its printing rate is often 600 lines per minute, but many print up to 1,000 lines per minute.

The speeds mentioned here are for ordinary everyday computers. They are not even close to the maximum found in really large computers.

The diagram below shows how instructions and data move from one unit to another.

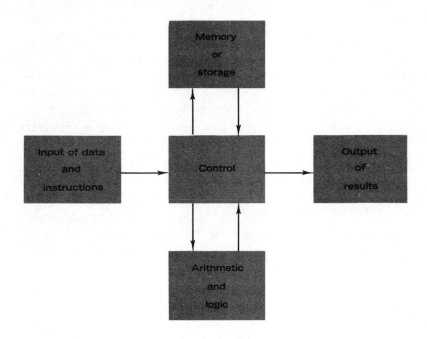

Many computers can store 1 to 4 million bits in the memory. Newer machines have even larger capacity. All computer makers try to create as vast a memory as possible.

The hidden parts of the control unit consist of a maze of

wires (see illustration below), electronic components including thousands of transistors (the IBM 7090, a larger computer, has 44,000), and all kinds of electrical circuits. These parts are almost never handled unless something goes wrong with the computer.

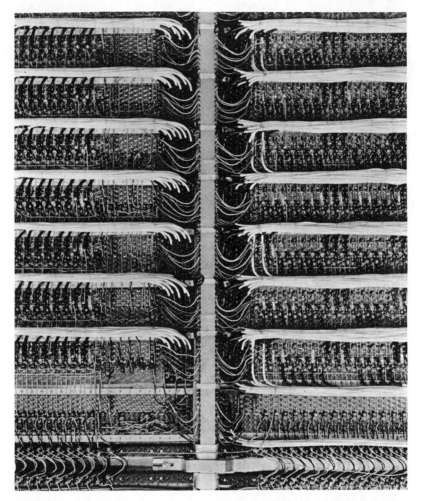

Behind the sleek exterior of a modern computer lies a jungle of electrical wiring. This is touched only in the event of serious breakdown. (IBM)

Circuit (left) contains transistors, diodes, resistors, and conductors. Casing (upper right) is protective. Size is less than ½ inch square. Common thumb tack (lower right) shows comparative size. (IBM)

The Logic of a Machine

The ability of a computer to use "logic," or reason, is at the heart of discussions about its ability to "think." We will examine the nature of its logic.

This arises from the computer's ability to compare and to obey an instruction that starts with "if." Here is an example.

The computer is instructed: Compare the number you are about to receive with that in your memory address 485–489. Act as follows:

1. If the numbers match (that is, are equal), send the number to A.

2. If the numbers are unequal, act as follows:

a. If the new number is higher, follow the instructions in address 245–249.

b. If the new number is lower, follow the instructions in address 241–243.

This type of instruction can become extremely complicated. It is what enables the computer to do things like playing chess.

We have already discussed how a computer does its calculations. Logic and arithmetic instructions can be mixed. Such a set of instructions could be: If the numbers are equal, add them.

An "everyday" computer can read and store data at the rate of more than 100,000 characters per second; it can do additions at that speed. Larger, or later, computers can far exceed this pace.

Holding a Conversation with a Computer

How do we "talk" to a computer whose vocabulary consists of numbers and some symbols? We give it orders by means of a *program*. We "talk" to it as we would to a child — clearly and without skipping any steps.

Before the *programer* starts to write a program, he must have a clear idea of what he wants the computer to do. As a guide to clear thinking, he draws a "picture" of the problem. This is called a flow chart, or flow diagram. Two examples are shown on pages 232 and 233. One is from an IBM manual — a flow chart for an imaginary program for an automatic record player. The other is a small section of a flow chart for an arithmetic problem. The size of a flow chart depends upon the complications of a problem.

With the flow chart before him, the programer starts to write his program. This will be in much greater detail. But in what "language"? Computers do not speak English — yet.

When the computer was an infant, one had to address it in its own language. But writing in numbers and symbols takes a lot of time, especially if no details can be skipped. Also, since programers are human, they made mistakes. Many hours were spent testing a program to see if the machine understood it.

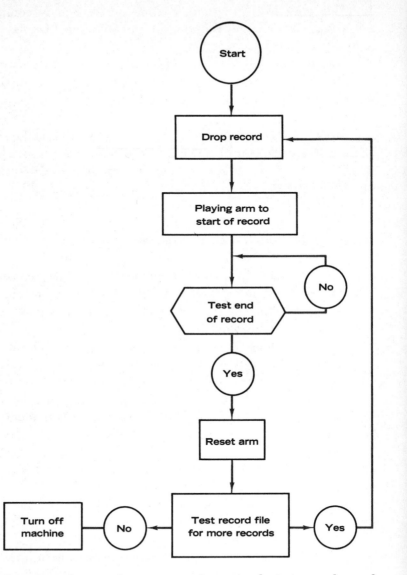

Flow chart showing the sequence of steps in playing several records on an automatic record player. Flow chart design precedes writing of a program as shown on page 235. (IBM)

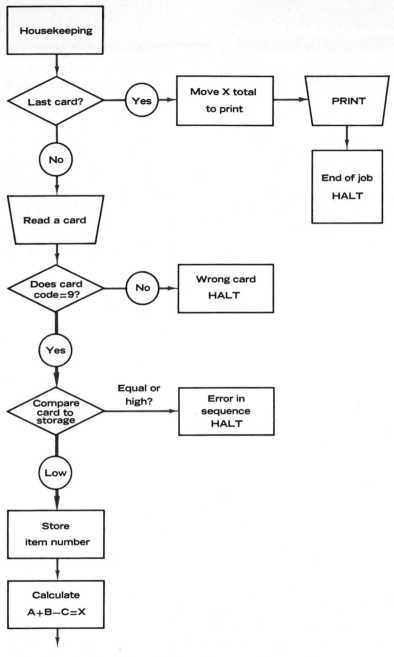

Section of a flow chart designed for an arithmetical operation.

Computer makers were busy trying to invent languages that were more like English and that the computer could understand. IBM invented FORTRAN, which stands for *Formula Translation*. This is still used. It also developed *Autocoder,* a language to be used with the 1401 computer.

The United States government faced a special problem. It bought computers from many makers, all using different languages. This meant training programers in one special language, and these are not easily learned. It spent, therefore, many millions of dollars developing a "universal language" that would be suitable for all computers. That language is COBOL, from *C*ommon *B*usiness-*O*riented *L*anguage.

These languages simplify the problem of talking to a computer. Here are some examples from Autocoder:

Autocoder symbol	Meaning to computer
CS	clear storage
R	read a punch card
P	punch a card
W	write (or print) a punch card
A	add

Since the computer still understands only numbers and some symbols, CS or R doesn't mean anything to it. There must be an interpreter between man and machine. This interpreter is called a *processor.* It takes the programer's language (in the form of a deck of punch cards) and "works" on them until it has translated them into another deck of punch cards that the computer can understand. There may now be 5 to 20 times as many cards as the processor started with.

While making the translation, the processor checks some of the programer's mistakes. Suppose that he wrote "HLAT 1" for "HALT 1." The machine will return his program because it is prepared to accept the word HALT 1 but not its variation — or anagram — HLAT 1.

The aim of every computer maker is to build a machine that will understand ordinary English — written or spoken. How far they have succeeded will be seen in the next section.

Form X24-1350-2
Printed in U.S.A.

IBM

Program _CASE STUDY S - PART I_

Programmed by ___HH___

Date _12/2/63_

INTERNATIONAL BUSINESS MACHINES CORPORATION

IBM 1401, 1410 AND 1440 DATA PROCESSING SYSTEMS
AUTOCODER CODING SHEET

Line 3 5 6	Label	Operation 15 16 20 21	OPERAND 25 30 35 40 45 50 55 60 65 70
0 1	DCF	DCW	@*@
0 2	COUNT	DC	#9
0 3	DATA	DA	1X100,G

A — ADD

OP Code	A Address	B Address
A	X X X X	X X X

This instruction causes the field at the A address to add algebraically to the field at the B address. (IBM)

C — COMPARE

OP Code	A Address	B Address
C	X X X X X	X X X

This instruction causes the field at the A address to be compared with the field at the B address.

The result of the compare (equal or unequal) is stored in the machine and then checked by a later instruction.

TOP: *Segment of a written program prepared by programer. These instructions are punched into cards.* (IBM)

BOTTOM: *Two basic programing codes, A and C, and what happens inside the computer when they are used.* (IBM)

The Computer of Tomorrow

Television and the computer were born at the same time. Everyone was excited about the first; the second was known only to a few people. What has happened since World War II, the approximate date of their birth?

The television picture is larger and clearer and can now be transmitted in color. It comes from a greater distance. A television signal can now be bounced off Telstar, the communications satellite. Television has changed the entertainment field. It is used in some industries. In department stores, it watches people to prevent stealing. It has helped us examine the surface of the moon. Perhaps its most important use is in education, though its real effects in this field are in the future.

Would the world be much different without television? Most thoughtful people would probably answer "No."

But no thoughtful person could possibly give the same answer to this question about computers. The computer may change our society. In some respects, it already has. The computer made it possible to orbit an astronaut. Other planets cannot be explored without it. The computer is changing science and mathematics and industry. The changes that have taken place as a result of the computer are as nothing compared with those that will almost certainly occur.

The computer's speed has been discussed. A billionth of a second is not the limit of its possibilities. Its accuracy, too, has been emphasized—billions of error-free calculations. But do computers ever break down? Do any of its hundreds of thousands of parts ever fail? Very, very seldom—but they do. Can anything be done about it?

Dr. William H. Pierce of Westinghouse Laboratories is one man who has been working on this problem. He describes his work in *Scientific American* of February 1964. The goal is a fool-proof computer that will "suppress errors." His method is complicated, but it will be explained briefly.

It involves "redundancy." This means "to repeat oneself,

to say the same thing in another way." For example, if you said, "I saw a huge giant," you would be *redundant*. Giants are always huge, so why add the word? Redundancy in machines means to have different parts that are able to do the same thing —to act as substitutes when something goes wrong.

At Westinghouse Laboratories, a model of a redundant machine has been built. Take a scissors and snip a bunch of wires—the machine still works. Why is a machine without error necessary? This is what Dr. Pierce said: "The most compelling reason is . . . that modern technology is increasingly dependent on the reliability of . . . equipment, much of it involving digital computing machinery; the survival of an orbiting astronaut, for example, depends on the rapid and accurate calculations of arithmetical problems on digital computers."

Machines That Read

Below is a part of a bank check. The numbers are codes for whose check it is, from what bank it came, and the amount of money involved.

A computer can read the numbers. But these are not ordinary numbers. They are written in a special way. Also, they are written with magnetized ink. That's why the computer can read them. But will a computer ever be able to read ordinary numbers and letters typed or written in regular pencil or ink?

IBM has an experimental machine that can already do some of this. In a trial at Tufts University, 200 people wrote down 100,000 ordinary numbers. Their only instruction was not to make them too unusual. The machine examined them and recognized 98.5 percent, about 98,500, of them correctly!

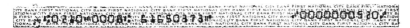

Codes on common bank checks are written with magnetized ink that a computer can "read." Digits at right represent $5.20.

The solution of this problem, and others, may make it possible some day to write programs in ordinary English.

Writing is fine, but talking is easier. Will we ever be able to say "Good morning" to a computer and get an answer? An experimental computer can recognize a voice—not any voice but one that it has been trained to hear. It's like a young puppy that recognizes only its master. The possibility that a computer will act in response to any voice is still some way off. But it has left fantasyland.

It is not known when a computer will be able to recognize your voice. But there is no doubt that, in *your* future, there will be a computer that will be able to read your writing.

At one of the leading engineering schools in the United States, a standard problem deals with highway construction. The entire problem had always been given to graduate stu-

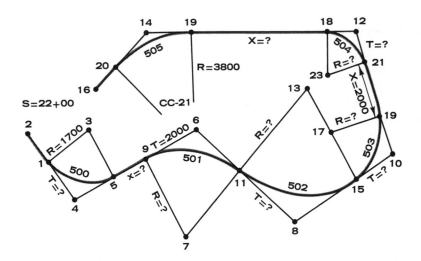

Engineering diagram was made by computer using COGO I. This is a program, not a piece of equipment. It helps design bridges or roads, using only 43 common engineering terms in its program. COGO stands for Coordinate Geometry for Civil Engineers. (IBM)

dents. One part of the problem was usually given to the senior class. In 1964, this part was given to the freshman class, instead. It was easily solved by them. In 1965, the entire problem, rather than a single part, will be given to the freshman class. It is expected that they will solve it satisfactorily.

Are present students brighter? No. The difference is that they are learning to use computers and are allowed to use them to help solve their problems.

In every university, in almost every branch of study, computers are being used more and more. Their use began with statistics, science, and mathematics, or all working together. It is spreading to economics, psychology, medical research, and most social sciences. Even archaeological problems have been solved by computer. The changes that the computer will bring to these fields cannot yet be fully foreseen, but it will affect all fields.

Information retrieval, or recall, has been mentioned briefly. Its importance may be judged by this statement that appeared in an IBM ad in 1962: "Each year . . . in the sciences, some 50,000 technical journals are published throughout the world. 100,000 research reports and 60,000 technical books are written." No scientist can keep up with this flood, even in his own small field. But somewhere in all this there may be *one article* that will help him in his work. It may have been written in Russian or Swedish. How will he know about it?

He needs someone to make it available. He needs someone to translate it. This help can come only from computers that translate, file, and retrieve.

Information retrieval means much more than "bringing back" articles and reports. It can be used as an important tool in many fields. One such field is medicine, where its use is being studied. It is possible to place into a computer's memory the symptoms of illnesses and diseases—also, their known treatment, including the many different drugs. What could then happen may be seen from the following example.

A patient walks into a doctor's office. The doctor's assistant prepares a punch card with the patient's history.

SEX: Male   AGE: 14 years   WEIGHT: 125 pounds   HEIGHT: 65 inches

PREVIOUS ILLNESSES: measles, mumps   OPERATIONS: tonsils removed

SYMPTOMS: temperature 102 degrees   FATIGUE: present

HEADACHE: present   THROAT: red   TONGUE: coated

There may be other codes.

The punch card is prepared and the information is sent to a central computer. Within seconds, a new card is returned by the computer. On it, in coded form, is the following:

DIAGNOSIS: patient has a bad cold

TREATMENT: two aspirins every 4 hours; plenty of liquid; bed rest

A patient's cardiogram (a graph of the action of the heart) was taken by a machine wired to a computer. It was taken in one city and sent *directly,* as it was being taken, to another city where it was diagnosed. The diagnosis was then relayed to the patient's hospital for appropriate treatment. Computer systems have been prepared for large hospitals. These will take readings directly from instruments (including special thermometers that work far faster than the ordinary kind) attached to a patient's body. If drugs are needed, the request goes directly to the hospital's pharmacy. The computer will also remind nurses when and how much medicine to give the patient.

Any discussion of the computer's place in the world of tomorrow seems like science fiction. Can you imagine the effect of a machine that can be used in so many fields? That does billions of things a second? That almost never makes a mistake? That almost never breaks down? That can read your handwriting? That can obey your oral instruction? That can store in its memory all the information in any given field? What fiction writer can top this? But we must realize that this is no longer fiction!

The computer made it possible to orbit an astronaut. It makes it possible for man to think of landing elsewhere in the universe. It does this not merely by making the calculations; it can exercise *direct* control. Outer space is an exciting frontier. But, here on earth, the frontiers of man's mind are also being stretched wider and wider.

Automation

In 1956, the New York State Department of Labor studied the recreation industry in the state. It reported that about 7,000 pinboys were employed in bowling alleys. There were also 170 pinchasers. In 1960, another study of the industry reported 900 pinboys and 750 pinchasers. If you bowl, you know that today a machine — an automatic pinspotter — sets up the pins in the alley. Only one or two human pinspotters are needed to assist the machine.

In four years, an automatic machine replaced the pinboy, wiping out 6,100 jobs in only one state in one occupation. This loss of pinboy jobs was slightly offset by a gain of about 600 jobs for pinspotters.

The familiar coal miner with a lamp on his cap and a pick in his hand is fast disappearing. Giant machines now strip the coal from the seams, or coal beds, of the mine. In the United States, in about fifteen years, over 350,000 miners have been eliminated.

This is one part of the automation process — the replacement of men by machines. Machines have always been used to do men's work. But, in automation, the *rate* of replacement has been enormously speeded up. Entire occupations, as in the above examples, are almost wiped out in a short time. The American economy faces a period of adjustment that will continue for many years, perhaps well into the 1970's. There are signs that the seriousness of the problem is recognized and that positive steps will be taken to meet it.

This side of automation is not properly the subject here. We are concerned with the use of machines—computers—to operate other machines. This is the automation of the future. Although it has already had important effects, the real effects lie ahead. Many books have been written on the subject. Here it will be discussed briefly to illustrate the part that computers will play.

Dr. Richard Bellman, a mathematician, wrote in *Scientific American* of September 1964: "In industry . . . it is estimated that about 500 computers . . . for process control are now installed or on order. Five years ago scarcely a dozen such machines were in service."

To this may be added the prediction of E. M. Grabbe of Bunker-Ramo Corporation, a computer manufacturer: By 1970 he expects that there will be 4,000 such machines. This indicates the importance of the operation.

These computers control the machines that make things. If you can, visit an oil refinery. You will see giant machines and pipes and tubes reaching into the sky. At night, their glow is visible from miles away. You will see a wealth of machinery— but almost no people. A few, in a control room, watch computers making calculations and printing out graph lines. Sometimes the men operate some switches.

In 1963, about one-third of the oil industry operated by computer.

The author visited, in 1964, a plant that produced a special type of concrete "pebble" used in construction. An oven as tall as a six-story building heated them to exact temperatures. The cooling and the piling onto small mountains of different-sized "pebbles" were controlled by computer. Even the loading onto barges on a river hundreds of yards away was automatic. Almost no men were around, except in a small control tower. These men watched wavy graphs prepared by computers.

The author has watched the production of parts for one of the most popular cameras in the world controlled by computer.

Dr. Bellman, mentioned before, describes a steel plant in England that began production in 1964. It makes use of three computers.

The first computer receives customers' orders and classifies them by type. It then calculates a three-week program for the steel furnaces and rolling mills. It also keeps track of progress. This is production planning.

The second computer takes over when the "billet" of steel (the amount being produced) has been produced. It then prepares a full set of instructions for treatment of the steel. It actually supervises the rolling mill which shapes the steel forms.

The third computer receives measurements of billet size. It computes how they should be cut to keep waste to a minimum.

The New York Times, in 1962, reported an interesting use of computers in another field: the transmission of materials by pipeline. These stretch across the United States and other countries. Among the things they carry are: natural gas, oil, gasoline, oxygen, nitrogen, alcohol, molasses, latex (liquid rubber), helium gas. Below are some extracts (sections) from the article.

One man, sitting at the controls of a vast communications network in Tulsa, Oklahoma, can direct a 2,000-mile pipeline journey of propane gas from New Mexico to Wisconsin and Minnesota.

Measurement of flow rates, pressure, and dozens of other variables . . . can be collected half a continent away and flashed to the dispatchers for analysis, often aided by an electronic computer.

The fast and uninterrupted flow of information has made analysis and control of pipeline flow by computer possible, while the increase in needed information has made the computer necessary. In addition, computers help design new pipelines by calculating the materials and equipment needed and by simulating the workings of a complex pipeline system.

The most important words in the article are the first two: "One man . . ."

These goods were once carried by railroads. It is easy to imagine that many railroad jobs were wiped out.

The Sabre system of American Airlines has been mentioned. This $30,000,000 computer network will handle all the company's airplane reservations. In 1965, when it went into full operation, it replaced 1,018 reservation clerks and 85 supervisors.

A machine that can do *in one minute* the calculations that a man can do in a year of eight-hour days can be expected to have a severe effect upon clerical occupations.

None of this has been brought about by advanced computers, which are now in experimental stages. They will aggravate the problems that already exist. For example, what will happen to thousands of mail-sorters in post offices and mail rooms when a computer can read ordinary handwriting?

The United States Department of Labor and nongovernment experts have estimated that, in 1964, automation was eliminating between 1,500,000 and 2,000,000 jobs a year. In 1964, President Johnson appointed a committee to study the effects of automation on the American economy.

Some companies that become automated try to place the people affected in other jobs. But two things must be considered:

1. The jobs that have been wiped out (reservation clerks, for example) no longer exist as opportunities for employment.

2. Not all the affected can be placed in jobs in the same company. Some have skills that are no longer needed. (This happened when meat-packers automated.) The government has a program to retrain some for other work. Many remain unemployed.

Who are the people most seriously affected? They are: those with little skill; people who move from rural to urban areas; and, above all, *those with little education*. These are the people, usually, with the least ability to adjust to a changing society. They are people who do routine jobs. Almost any routine job can be done better and faster by a computer.

The brighter future will belong to those who are well educated and fully trained. This will be truer tomorrow than it ever was before in American history. For those now planning their future, it is wiser to think of being master of the computer than of being mastered by one.

Can a Computer Think?

Many years ago, an eminent man made a forecast of what the computer would do some day. Among other things, he wrote that a computer would be chess champion of the world. In 1965, this prediction was a long way from coming true. Though computers can play chess, as we have said, there is no computer in sight that could make this come true. Whatever else may happen, a human being will be chess champion of the world for a long time to come.

Men often exaggerate the possibilities of a revolutionary development when it first appears. Then it is found that there is a limit to its potential.

In the same circumstances, men rush to compare machines to the human body or its parts. The heart has been compared to a clock, the camera to an eye. An auto engine and the human body have been paired. It is almost inevitable that men compare the computer with the brain. They then ask, "Can a computer think?"

A wide range of ideas has been expressed on this subject. It is not possible to discuss them here. But those who tend to answer "Yes" generally follow one line of reasoning. They start by asking, "What is thought?" Then they analyze it in mechanical terms. A stimulus — something that causes you to act, to do something in response — they say, travels along a nerve path. It reaches the brain. The brain then searches out a response to this stimulus. This, they say, is the pattern of thought. It is, they continue, the pattern of the computer.

This brief summary does not do full justice to these ideas, but it is the heart of it.

Science does not yet know very much about how the brain functions, but some things are known. It is known, for example, that the brain continues to function when many nerve cells are injured. In some way, these cells are bypassed. At the same time, the body begins to repair the damaged nerves.

Whether the brain reacts only to one stimulus at a time is open to question. Our mind may be occupied with an absorbing problem. Stimuli may be rushing to the brain. But a threat to our life will rush in stimuli of a higher order. These will be given priority, an immediate go-ahead signal.

The brain also seems to operate at more than one *level* at the same time. Many writers, especially James Joyce, whose work you may read some day, have explored this. A man talks to another and makes intelligent answers. At the same time, he is thinking of other things that have nothing to do with the conversation.

You may have experienced the same thing. Assume that you are coming home from a movie or a concert. A friend stops you and asks, "How was it?" You start to tell him. At the same time, you are thinking, "Gee, my mother will wonder where I am." While this is going through your mind, you remember that you haven't finished your math homework. The word "home" reminds you that you were asked to bring home a quart of milk. Throughout all this, the conversation with your friend goes on. It's as if there were a blend of stimuli. There is no logical order. It is uncoordinated thought, not joined together by a single topic. And to each stimulus, there is a different order of response.

When a computer plays chess, all its "attention" is on the game. A chess-playing man may remember that he must take his brown suit to the cleaner and his son for a violin lesson.

Another characteristic of human thought is its ability to leap-frog or jump or skip steps. A good deal of thought is not in sequence. It is disconnected or uncoordinated. We "see" ahead before we have examined all the possibilities. Sometimes we call this a "hunch" or "intuition."

This is not the opposite of what is often called "clear thinking." Some of mankind's greatest achievements have come from this kind of thought. Great writers or mathematicians or scientists know what it is. It is often the most creative kind of thinking.

In a good dictionary, the definition of "to think" requires several paragraphs. Among the synonyms are the following:

> to fancy
> to picture
> to imagine
> to meditate
> to ponder over
> to reflect upon
> to form or have an idea
> to form connected ideas of any kind

The only kind of "thought" that can be attributed to the computer is the last: to form connected ideas. But it is "ideas" only in the simplest meaning of the word. It is man's ability to form ideas from uncoordinated thoughts that casts doubt upon a machine's ability to think.

In a foreword to his translation of *Madame Bovary*, a great French novel by Gustave Flaubert, Francis Steegmuller discusses Flaubert's "errors" of time, place, etc. He says of these: ". . . they will disturb only those who confuse artistic realism with mechanical faithfulness to detail."

A machine has "mechanical faithfulness to detail." We expect this of it. It does not have the ability to go beyond accuracy to creative artistry.

We have discussed the computer's ability to translate from other languages. This is an important function of a computer, and it is successful when it makes a faithful and accurate translation. The more dictionaries and encyclopedias that can be put into the computer's memory, the better the translation will be.

But is this "thought"? Can it ever equal human translation? Here is Mr. Steegmuller on this subject: "To find out, one exhausts dictionaries, encyclopedias and reference librarians; one telephones to friends, acquaintances and strangers; one consults practitioners of various trades, both at home and abroad."

What resources are left to the human translator after all this has been done? One thing: thought. This is the element that is missing in machine translation.

One other topic is worth discussing. It was said earlier that you cannot beat a computer at ticktacktoe. In this child's game, the number of possible moves is very limited. They can easily be programed. The game is not even "worthy" of a real computer. However, a simple, hand-wired ticktacktoe machine that couldn't be beaten was invented. It could always achieve at least a draw. Aside from his "know-how" about electricity, the machine had cost the inventor about $10.

Checkers is a more complicated game, but it is still possible to program almost all the defensive and offensive moves. A computer has played to a draw with a state checkers champion.

Chess is a game with which we associate higher levels of thought. Claude E. Shannon, a pioneer contributor to computer theory, did a great deal of experimental work with a chess-playing computer. Here are some of his statements on this problem, which appeared in an article entitled "A Chess-Playing Machine" from *The World of Mathematics*, Vol. 4, by James R. Newman:

. . . the total number of possible variations in an average game [about 40 moves for each player] is about 10^{120}. A machine calculating one variation each millionth of a second would require over 10^{95} years to decide on its first move.

The number 10^{95} has 95 zeros!

. . . with computer speeds at present available, the machine could not explore all the possibilites for more than two moves ahead for each side.

How does the computer become a chess player? Does it learn "from scratch," as do you and I?

Dr. Shannon continues: "The program designer can employ here the principles of correct play that have been evolved by expert chess players."

In employing a computer to play chess, we call upon its mechanical attention to detail, but to say that a computer produces thought is like saying that a television screen produces people.

Man is always in control of the machine, even in its most complicated and "freest" activities — simulation and the making of mathematical and scientific models. The machine may seem to be acting independently, but it is following man's instructions.

Here is a parallel. A father takes his young child to a park where there is a wide meadow. He says to the child, "Go and play." The child proceeds to wander over the meadow. Another person, passing the child and seeing no one nearby, remarks, "Strange that such a young child should wander about free." But is the child "free"? In the background is the parent who has made all the conditions of the child's freedom.

In *The New York Times* of August 3, 1964, there was an advertisement by IBM. It began, "Computers don't think but in the hands of thinking men . . ."

In the hands of a thinking man, tools enlarge the man.

It is the author's hope that you have gained some knowledge of new fields, new things, new areas of thought. Today, statistics is a partner to every science — physical, biological, social. It has become an indispensable tool to the educated person. The computer and statistics are now permanently bound together.

You stand at the gates of a new world. Change is everywhere — change in nations, change in ideas. There are new sources of energy of fantastic power in the atom, new frontiers in space that challenge man's mind as well as his courage, new tools such as the computer, the like of which man has never had in his hands before.

Sometimes the picture of the emerging world is frightening. There is danger, it is true. But there is also hope. Which will be realized—the danger or the hope—will be decided by man himself. Educated, thinking men with knowledge of these developments will play an important part in shaping the decision.

ANSWER SECTION

The Answer Section has three principal objectives:

1. To answer the specific questions that were raised in the main body of the book.

2. To expand the discussion of some topics.

3. To discuss a few new subjects that are closely related to others that were treated earlier.

CHAPTER 1, *page 22: Mickey Mantle's home runs*
Problem 1. Mickey Mantle hit the most home runs in the year in which the graph reaches its peak, or highest point. That was in 1961, when he hit 54 — if you don't already know it from a baseball record book.

The simplest way to read a graph such as this is to place a ruler at the peak — if you are interested in finding a maximum — and line it up to lie parallel with any horizontal line; then read the scale to the left of the graph.

Problem 2. To find the number of home runs in 1960, first locate the year on the horizontal scale. Then move upward until you reach the line of the graph. Using a ruler as described above, read the vertical scale to the left. You will find that in 1960 Mickey Mantle hit 40 home runs.

CHAPTER 1, *page 30: Interpreting a pie chart*
Problem 1. *Percent for agriculture.* The entire pie chart represents $1.
Of this amount, 3 cents will be spent for agriculture. This is the same
as saying that 3 percent of the total budget will be spent for this service.

Although the method of changing a fraction to a percent is discussed in detail later in the book, this is the way it is done here:

$$\frac{3 \text{ cents}}{100 \text{ cents}} \times 100 = 3 \text{ percent}$$

Problem 2. *National defense in degrees of a circle.* National defense
expenditures will account for 40 cents of a one-dollar pie, or 40/100.
Find this fraction of the 360° of a circle – any circle – and you will
know how many degrees will be allotted to defense.

$$\frac{40}{100} \times 360° = \frac{14{,}400}{100} = 144°$$

This is exactly how such a pie chart is planned.
How many degrees are allotted to agriculture?

$$\frac{3}{100} \times 360° = \frac{1{,}080}{100} = 10.8 \text{ (approximately 11 degrees)}$$

If you know the amounts or percents allocated to each of a group of
items, you need only a ruler and a protractor to construct a pie chart.

It was said that the 1966 budget will be about 100 billion dollars.
Knowing this, you can now find the approximate amount, in dollars,
that is set aside for each item. For example, 4 cents of the dollar, or
4 percent, is to be spent on space exploration. Therefore, *the dollar
amount* is equal to 4 percent of 100 billion dollars. This comes out to
4 billion dollars, very close to the actual amount.

CHAPTER 2, *page 45: The standard deviation for Jane's class*
The use of symbols is common in mathematics and in all the sciences, as well as in statistics. Letters of the Greek alphabet are very
often used. Some of these have the same meaning in all fields; others
have special meanings. Before you go very far in any of these fields,
the Greek alphabet will become as familiar to you as your own.

Below are the symbols necessary in the calculation of the standard deviation. They are common to statistical work.

X This represents an individual value or observation. Here, X stands for the individual class mark. If there were other observations associated with the marks, perhaps age of student, they would be represented by Y.

$\bar{X}$ A capital letter X with a line above it is read "X bar." It stands for the mean, or average, of the X values. If there were Y values, their mean would be shown as $\bar{Y}$.

f This is the symbol for the frequency with which an observation occurs.

N The total number of cases is shown by this letter. It is the sum of the frequencies of all observations.

x This is called "little x." It stands for the *difference* between the mean and an individual value. The difference is called the *deviation* from the mean. In some books this type of deviation is shown by d, called "little d."

Σ This symbol is the Greek capital letter sigma. It stands for "the sum of" or the total of a set of numbers. It is used in this way in all sciences.

σ This is the Greek lower-case, or "small," letter sigma. It is always referred to as "sigma." In statistics it stands for the standard deviation that we are about to calculate. The formula for the standard deviation is

$$\sigma = \sqrt{\frac{\Sigma f(x^2)}{N}}$$

$\sqrt{}$ This is a square-root sign. Square roots are discussed in Chapter 3 and in a later part of the Answer Section. The sign asks: What number, multiplied by itself, will equal the amount under the square-root sign?

The next step is to find the values to use in the formula. (*Reminder:* $\bar{X}$, the mean, of Jane's class was 65.)

Column 1	Column 2	Column 3	Column 4	Column 5
			The squares	
		Deviation: difference	*of the*	
Mark on	*Number of*	*between marks*	*values in*	*Column 2*
test	*students*	*and mean*	*column 3*	*× column 4*
X	f	x	x^2	$f(x^2)$
85	1	+20	400	400
80	1	+15	225	225
75	3	+10	100	300
70	7	+5	25	175
65	5	0	0	0
60	3	−5	25	75
50	4	−15	225	900
40	1	−25	625	625
	$N = 25$			$\Sigma\, f(x^2) = 2{,}700$

(*Reminder:* It was not necessary to enter the plus (+) and minus (−) signs in column 3. The multiplication of 2 negative numbers gives a positive result: $- \times - = +$.)

The values can now be substituted in the equation:

$$\sigma = \sqrt{\frac{\Sigma\, f(x^2)}{N}} = \sqrt{\frac{2{,}700}{25}} = \sqrt{108} = 10.4 \text{ (approximately)}$$

It was said in Chapter 2 that the range between the mean plus 2 standard deviations $(\bar{X} + 2\sigma)$ and the mean minus 2 standard deviations $(\bar{X} - 2\sigma)$ would include 95 percent of the cases. This should be true for a standard deviation (σ) with a value of 10.4. On page 45 a value of 10 was used. This was an approximation to test the 95 percent inclusion statement.

$$\bar{X} + 2\sigma = 65 + 2 \times 10.4 = 65 + 20.8 = 85.8$$
$$\bar{X} - 2\sigma = 65 - 2 \times 10.4 = 65 - 20.8 = 44.2$$

Only one mark—40—falls outside the limits of 44.2 and 85.8. Thus, again, 24 out of 25 values fall within this range. This is equal to 96 percent of the cases, very close to the expected 95 percent.

CHAPTER 2, *page 45:* **If everyone scores 65 on a test**

The standard deviation is a special type of average that measures deviations from the mean. If everyone scored 65, there would be no deviation. Sigma (σ) would, therefore, be zero.

This is not a situation that you are likely to meet in real life. In life, in any of its forms, there is difference. Sometimes it may not appear to be so at first glance. However, careful study or scientific measurement reveals differences. Even when there is a deliberate attempt to create identity or uniformity, the result is diversity or difference.

What could seem as alike as millions of pennies fresh from the mint? They are created to be identical. Yet, if they were examined with instruments fine enough to measure 1/10,000th of an inch or an ounce, differences would come to light. For *practical* purposes, such as gum machines, they may be alike; for *scientific* purposes they are individual objects.

The standard deviation is a measure of the degree of difference.

CHAPTER 2, *page 47:* **A weighted average**

The calculation of the simple mean is fairly easy. The numbers, or observations, are added and then divided by the number of observations. Very often, however, it is necessary to use *weights* to obtain the true mean of a set of observations. Weights are used in calculating one of the most important statistics in the United States.

Each month, the Bureau of Labor Statistics of the U.S. Department of Labor announces the previous month's Consumers' Price Index. If you listen to news broadcasts, you may have heard an announcer say, "The Consumers' Price Index last month rose to 114.3, an increase of two-tenths (0.2) of a point for the month. The Bureau of Labor Statistics states that higher prices for food and automobiles were mainly responsible for the rise."

This index, usually referred to as C.P.I., plays an important part in the American economy. Labor-union contracts with industry often state that hourly rates of pay for their workers are to change automatically with changes in the index. A rise of 0.2 points in the index may mean that an auto worker's hourly pay will go up by 2 or 3 cents. Thus, his weekly wages may go up by a dollar or more. This may not strike you as being very much, but it can mean a tremendous amount of money to a company such as General Motors with hundreds of thousands of workers.

The Consumers' Price Index is a measure of *price change* in items bought for their own use by wage and clerical workers living in cities or suburbs. Money spent by families or single persons living alone, no matter how much they earn, is included in the calculation of the index. There are only two conditions they must meet:

1. At least half the income must be earned in wage or clerical work.

2. One member of a family must have worked at least 37 weeks during the year.

The *source* of the income is important; the *amount* is not.

Agents of the Bureau of Labor Statistics are constantly pricing the items people buy in 50 large urban areas — the cities and their suburbs. Needless to say, every store in these areas cannot be visited. The pricing is done by means of a *probability sample* of stores. (Sampling is discussed in Chapter 4.)

What is priced? Prices are obtained for a fixed set of things that are normally bought by consumers. This is often referred to as a *market basket* of goods. But this market basket is so huge that it includes among its hundreds of items such things as a house and the cost of your (future) college education.

The final index is obtained by means of an extremely complicated set of weights. The weights are based upon the size of the cities where the pricing is done, the way people spend the money in their budget, and many other factors. We will consider a simple imaginary example of one set of weights. It is not too different in idea, however, from the method actually used.

Example. Agents are sent to price a 1-pound package of standard white bread in five different cities. They find these average prices:

City	Population	Average bread price, cents
New York	7,781,984	26
Chicago	3,550,404	24
Los Angeles	2,479,015	25
Philadelphia	2,002,512	24
Minneapolis	482,872	21
	16,296,787	

By adding the 5 prices and dividing by 5, a simple mean is obtained. This is: $1.20/5 = 24 cents per package. Such a mean is called an *unweighted* mean. But it is not the true mean of the price of bread in the 5 cities. New York City has about 16 times the population of Minneapolis; its residents pay 5 cents more per package. There is every reason to believe that New Yorkers will eat 16 times as much bread as residents of Minneapolis and about 4 times as much as Philadelphians. Therefore, the true mean can be obtained only by taking into account the relative populations.

One way to obtain a true, or weighted, mean is to multiply the bread price in a city by its population, add the products, and then divide by the total population of all cities.

THE SUM OF
$$\overline{}$$
$$\downarrow$$
$$\frac{\Sigma \text{ population} \times \text{price}}{\text{total population}}$$

This would involve tremendous multiplications. They would take too much of a computer's time and space. A simpler way is to change the individual populations of the cities to a basis of 100. This is done by calculating each city's population as a percent of the total population.

Although this requires division of large numbers, it has to be done only once. The 50 areas where the pricing is done are fixed. The weights, once calculated, would not change for some time.

This is the final table, including the weights:

Column 1 *City*	*Column 2* *Approximate percent* *of total population*	*Column 3* *Price, cents*	*Column 4* *Column 2* *× column 3*
New York	*Weight:* 48	26	1,248
Chicago	22	24	528
Los Angeles	15	25	375
Philadelphia	12	24	288
Minneapolis	3	21	63
	100		$\Sigma = 2,502$

$$\text{Weighted average:} \frac{\Sigma \text{ weight} \times \text{price}}{\text{total weights}} = \frac{2,502}{100} = 25.02 \text{ cents}$$

To find the weighted average, the weight of the population was substituted for the actual population. The result is exactly the same.

The weighted average price of a pound of packaged white bread is a little more than a cent higher than the unweighted average — 25.02 as against 24.00 cents.

Considering the importance of the Consumers' Price Index, you realize that a penny's difference on a package of bread is important.

CHAPTER 3, *page 61: Solving an equation for an unknown value*
The solution of the equation that follows requires only the ability to pay strict attention to detail.

$$a^3 + 2a^2b + ab + 10c + 2c^2 - 20 = 118$$

Find the value of b if $a = 2$ and $c = 5$.

Step 1. Substitute the known values of a and c in the equation, maintaining the powers of the numbers and their signs (+ or −).

$$(2^3) + (2 \times 2^2b) + (2b) + (10 \times 5) + (2 \times 5^2) - (20) = 118$$

Step 2. Change the powers of the numbers into multiplication form. You may skip this step if you know how to work with powers of numbers. Then, move to step 3.

$$(2 \times 2 \times 2) + (2 \times 2 \times 2b) + (2b) + (10 \times 5) + (2 \times 5 \times 5) - 20 = 118$$

Step 3. Complete the multiplications.

$$8 + 8b + 2b + 50 + 50 - 20 = 118$$

Step 4. Add together the b values as well as the numbers on the left side of the equation.

$$10b + 88 = 118$$

Step 5. Subtract 88 from each side.

$$10b + 88 - 88 = 118 - 88$$
$$10b = 30$$

Step 6. Simplify and solve for b.

$$\frac{10b}{10} = \frac{10}{10} \times b = \frac{30}{10}$$
$$b = 3$$

CHAPTER 3, *page 66: Square roots*

Numbers with decimal places. In simple division, the presence of numbers after a decimal point does not change the usual method. For example:

$$
\begin{array}{r}
3.75 \\
25\overline{)93.75} \\
-75 \\
\hline
18\,7 \\
-17\,5 \\
\hline
1\,25 \\
-1\,25 \\
\hline
\end{array}
$$

In finding square roots of numbers with decimal places, the same general rules apply with minor exceptions. These are:

1. The general rule, as discussed in Chapter 3, is that the numbers must be arranged and handled in pairs of digits. When numbers with decimal places are involved, the whole number and the decimal part are arranged separately.

Example. Find the square root of 375.1693.

The numbers would be arranged as follows:

$$\sqrt{03\ 75\ .\ 16\ 93}$$

The zero before the 3 is only for illustration. It is not needed.

2. When there is an odd number of digits after the decimal point, a zero is tacked on at the end to create an even number of digits *after the decimal point.* This, as you probably know, does not change the value.

$$.1 = \frac{1}{10} \qquad .10 = \frac{10}{100} = \frac{1}{10}$$

As many zeros as necessary can be added in this way without changing the value of the number.

Example. Find the square root of 725.327.

The numbers would be arranged as follows:

$$\sqrt{07\ 25\ .\ 32\ 70}$$

A zero has been added at the end, but the value of the number has not changed.

Problem. Find the square root of 742.5625.

Step 1. Starting from the right, break up the whole number into pairs of digits. Then, starting from the left—from the decimal point—break up the fractional number into pairs of digits.

$$\sqrt{7\ 42\ .\ 56\ 25}$$

There will be as many digits in your answer as there are pairs of numbers. "Seven" is counted as a pair; it is really "07."

Step 2. What is the highest number, multiplied by itself, that can go into 7? The answer is, of course, 2. Place it in quotient and divisor and multiply.

$$
\begin{array}{r}
2\phantom{\sqrt{7\ 42\ .\ 56\ 25}} \\
2\sqrt{7\ 42\ .\ 56\ 25} \\
\underline{-4} \\
3
\end{array}
$$

(*Remember:* The remainder can be greater than the divisor in calculating square roots.)

Step 3. From the dividend, bring down the next pair of digits to join the remainder.

$$
\begin{array}{r}
2\phantom{\sqrt{7\ 42\ .\ 56\ 25}} \\
2\sqrt{7\ 42\ .\ 56\ 25} \\
\underline{-4} \\
3\ 42
\end{array}
$$

Step 4. Double the quotient and bring it down as a new divisor. Leave space to its right for another digit.

$$
\begin{array}{r}
2\phantom{\sqrt{7\ 42\ .\ 56\ 25}} \\
2\sqrt{7\ 42\ .\ 56\ 25} \\
\underline{-4} \\
4\_3\ 42
\end{array}
$$

The "4_" now stands for "40 something." It will change to the 40's as soon as you fill the space.

Step 5. What number can now be placed in the quotient and into the unfilled units' position of the divisor so that when the whole divisor and this number are multiplied, the product will be closest to (but not over) 342? Either directly or by trial and error the new number is found to be 7. Multiply only the new number in the quotient by the new divisor (7 × 47).

```
        2  7
   2 √7 42 . 56 25
      −4
  47 ⌐3 42
     −3 29
        13
```

(*Reminder:* At this point, don't forget to enter a decimal point in the quotient, your answer place.)

Step 6. Bring down the next pair of numbers (56). The fact that they follow the decimal point does not change the operation. Double the quotient and bring it down, leaving a space to its right, exactly as in step 4.

```
         2  7 .
    2 √7 42 . 56 25
       −4
   47 ⌐3 42
      −3 29
   54     13 56
```

Step 7. Follow step 5. You will find that the next number in the quotient is 2 because 2 × 542 is less than 1356.

```
          2  7 .  2
     2 √7 42 . 56 25
        −4
    47 ⌐3 42
       −3 29
  542 ⌐  13  56
        −10  84
          2  72
```

Step 8. Complete the calculation after bringing down the next pair.

```
              2  7 . 2  5
        2 √7 42 . 56 25
          −4
     47 ⌐3 42
         −3 29
   542 ⌐  13  56
         −10  84
  5445⌐   2  72 25
          2  72 25
```

The process is now complete because every pair has been brought down. The square root of 742.5625 is 27.25. This can be checked by multiplying 27.25 by itself.

The square roots of numbers that do not come out "even." In saying this, as will be shown, we are talking about numbers whose square roots have no end. The result of the calculation is an approximation — as close as we want it — of the square root.

First, let us examine some interesting characteristics of numbers that have integral or whole number square roots. These numbers are called perfect squares. The root is shown in parentheses.

Column 1 *What is the* *square root of*	*Column 2* *Difference between number* *and one just above it*
0 (0)	—
1 (1)	1
4 (2)	3
9 (3)	5
16 (4)	7
25 (5)	9
36 (6)	11
49 (7)	13
64 (8)	15
81 (9)	17
100 (10)	19

Do you notice the progression in column 2? There is a constant difference of 2. We can easily answer the question: What is the next number whose square root is an integer? Obviously, it is the sum of the last number with a whole-number square root (100) plus the next number in the progression in column 2, or 21. The next number whose square root is an integer is 121; its square root is 11.

We can also find the next number in another way. Knowing that the square of 11 is 121, what is the *square* (not square root) of 12? This will be the next number that has an integral square root.

It is the sum of 121, 11, and 12.

121 the preceding square
 11 The number whose square preceded
 12 the next number whose square is wanted
___
144

You probably know that the square root of 144 is 12.

This has no extraordinary importance. It does, however, reveal some of the inner logic of numbers, and it shows that it can be fun to play around with them.

We now return to our basic problem.

Problem. Find the square root of 2.

The problem is not changed by writing it this way:

$$\sqrt{2.00\ 00\ 00\ 00\ 00\ 00\ 00}$$

As many zeros as are necessary can be added after the decimal point. The number of meaningful digits in the answer depends upon the problem. Very often a problem is worded: Calculate to 5 *significant digits*. This means that there should be 5 digits in the quotient. For example, if an answer has to be given in dollars and cents, it is wasteful of time and effort to give the answer as $2.7513. However, if the answer had to be *in tenths of a cent*, it would be given as $2.751.

The calculation of the square root of 2, to 7 decimal places, shows it to be 1.4142135.

There is no exact answer to $\sqrt{2}$, no matter how far the calculation is extended. As the calculation continues, adding more and more places after the decimal point, the result comes closer and closer to the $\sqrt{2}$, but it never reaches it. The outer limits are approached, but the answer is always an approximation.

The square root of 2 is an *irrational number*. An irrational number is a real number, but it cannot be expressed in integers ("whole" numbers, not fractions) or as quotients of integers.

The table below shows how closely 2 is approached as the calculation is extended to more and more decimal places and the result is squared.

Column 1	Column 2	Column 3	Column 4
			Difference between
Number of	*Square*	*The square root*	*column 3 and*
places after	*root*	*squared*	*the number 2*
decimal point	*of 2*	*(col. 2 × col. 2)*	*(2 − column 3)*
1	1.4	1.96	.04
2	1.41	1.9881	.0119
3	1.414	1.999396	.0006
4	1.4142	1.99996164	.000038
5	1.41421	1.9999899241	.000010
6	1.414213	1.999998409369	.0000016
7	1.4142135	1.99999982358225	.00000018
			(numbers rounded
			for convenience)

Column 4 shows how far away from or how close the answer is to 2. With 1 place after the decimal point in the square root, the result is 4/100 away from the "true" answer. With 5 places, the result is only 1/100,000 away. With 7 places, it is only a little more than 1 ten-millionth away. This is certainly closer than would be needed for most practical purposes. The numbers in column 3 are said to approach 2 *as a limit*—but they can never reach it mathematically.

This is true of all numbers whose square roots do not come out even.

CHAPTER 3, *page 135: Poisson distributions*
The formula for the Poisson distribution may look very frightening at first glance. But; as in many other situations in life, fear is eliminated by understanding. This is the formula:

$$P(y) = \frac{e^{-np} \times (np)^y}{y!}$$

The first simplification will be along the lines discussed in Chapter 3. There it was said that *n*, which stands for the number of tests, observations or experiments, must be very large. In other words, an event has many opportunities of taking place.

It was also said that *p* — the probability of the event happening — must be very small.

When these two conditions exist, the formula can be used. Then, *np*, or $n \times p$, is usually set to equal *m* ($n \times p = m$).

The formula can then be rewritten:

$$P(y) = \frac{e^{-m} \times m^y}{y!}$$

It now looks a little more manageable.

In Poisson distributions, *np* is also the mean. And the square root of *np* is equal to the standard deviation. Statisticians speak more often of the *variance*, which is equal to σ^2. It is beyond the range of this book to discuss variance, but this makes everything very tidy. Both mean and variance equal *np* or *m*.

The parts of the formula stand for the following:

1. $P(y)$: This merely means: What is the probability that an event with the value *y* will take place? (*y* can be 1, 2, 4, etc.)

2. e^{-m}: Any value to a negative power can be written as a fraction whose numerator is 1. Thus, e^{-m} is the same as $1/e^m$. The value of *m* has been discussed; it is equal to $n \times p$, usually expressed as a whole number.

In the value *e*, we meet an entirely new term. It has a fixed value of approximately 2.71828. The value is approximate because it is an irrational number similar to $\sqrt{2}$. The reason for the strange number is that *e* is the base of a set of values called *natural logarithms*.

Logarithms have an ancient history; they go back to the early seventeenth century. They were created to make calculations such as multiplication and division easier. Ordinary logarithms are based upon 10, the base of our number system. If one had to multiply 2,734 × 4,608, he would look up the logarithms of the two numbers in a table of logarithms, *add* them, and look up the sum in the same table for his answer. Division is similar, except that the two logarithms are subtracted. Today, with high-speed desk calculators, to say nothing of computers, this use of logarithms has lost its advantages. But logarithms still play a very important part in higher mathematics.

Natural logarithms, instead of being based upon 10, are based upon an approximate value of *e.* The reason for this will one day be discovered by those who go on to the study of calculus. But, mathematically, it is quite natural and necessary.

Therefore, e^{-m} is the same as $1/2.71828^m$, with whatever value m will have.

3. m^y: This explains itself. Whatever value m has is raised to a power equal to the value of y. Thus, if y equals 2, m^y will be m^2.

4. $y!$: We meet an old friend—factorial numbers. Again, the value set for y determines the factorial value given here. If y is equal to 2, then 2 factorial will be used.

Before we use the Poisson formula in a problem, here are two actual cases where predictions based upon the formula were almost identical with results actually found. The two situations, of tremendous importance in a historical sense, are reported by Prof. William Feller in his excellent book, *An Introduction to Probability Theory and Its Applications.*

Case 1. Three famous British scientists—Lord Rutherford, Chadwick, and Ellis—the first two Nobel Prize winners, performed a basic experiment with radioactive substances. These give off certain subatomic particles called alpha particles. The experiment was designed to observe how many particles reached a counter, a sensitive instrument that recorded them. There were 2,608 observations at time intervals of 7.5 seconds. On the next page are the results actually obtained and predictions based upon the Poisson formula.

Number of particles hitting the counter	Theoretical predictions of Poisson formula	Actual frequencies observed in the experiment
0	54.4	57
1	210.5	203
2	407.4	383
3	525.5	525
4	508.4	532
5	393.5	408
6	253.8	273
7	140.3	139
8	67.9	45
9	29.2	27
10 or more	17.1	16
	2,608.0	2,608

Such theoretical predictions are considered extremely close.

Case 2. During World War II, the Germans fired thousands of flying bombs—called buzz bombs—at London. An analysis was made of the number of hits made on 576 small areas. The actual hits are matched against predicted hits based upon the Poisson formula.

Number of hits on any area	Predictions based on Poisson formula	Actual number of areas receiving that many hits
0	226.7	229
1	211.4	211
2	98.5	93
3	30.6	35
4	7.1	7
5 or more	1.6	1
	575.9	576

Problem. This problem does not have the earth-shattering importance of atomic experiments or bomb hits, but it will make clear how the formula is used.

A soda-bottling plant turns out thousands of cases of fruit soda each day. Therefore, n is very large. Although the production is automatic the company has found, after a study of several days' production, that each day 2 cases of soda have been mislabeled. Sarsaparilla had a lemon and lime bottle cap and one case of grape soda was stated to be orange. With only 2 such cases in a day's production, p is small.

What is the probability (P) that a day's production will have no incorrectly labeled cases? Only 1 such case?

No (0) cases wrongly labeled:

n is large and unknown; p is small. Therefore, $np = m = 2$ (the number of errors).

$$P(y) = \frac{e^{-m} \times m^y}{y!}$$

$P(y)$ is the probability that y will have a value of $0 -$ no errors.

$$e^{-m} = (2.71828)^{-2} = \frac{1}{(2.71828)^2}$$

$m^y = 2^0 = 1$ (Any number to a zero power equals 1.)

$y! = 0! = 1$ (You may recall that 0! equals 1.)

Substituting in the formula,

$$P(0) = \frac{\dfrac{1}{(2.71828)^2} \times 2^0}{0!} = \frac{\dfrac{1}{7.389 \text{ (app.)}} \times 1}{1} = \frac{1}{7.389}$$

$$= 0.135 \text{ or } 13.5 \text{ percent}$$

Thus, on 13.5 percent of the days, there will be no mislabeled bottles.

Only 1 mislabeled case per day: The probability that $y = 1$.

$$P(1) = \frac{\dfrac{1}{(2.71828)^2} \times 2^1}{1!} = \frac{\dfrac{1}{7.389} \times 2}{1} = \frac{2}{7.389} = .271 = 27.1 \text{ percent}$$

On about 27 percent of the days, there will be only 1 mislabeled case. The Poisson formula that looked so forbidding at first glance turns out to be fairly simple in use. And, in situations where it applies, it is an extremely powerful tool for prediction.

CHAPTER 5, *page 222: Binary operations*

In Chapter 5 two binary numerals, 13_{ten} and 7_{ten}, were added, and the sum was shown to have the expected value of 20_{ten}.

*Binary value
according to position*

16	8	4	2	1
	1	1	0	1	= 13
	0	1	1	1	= 7
1	0	1	0	0	= 20

There is a "carry" in each step from right to left.

A multiplication operation in binary, the equivalent of $3_{ten} \times 2_{ten} = 6_{ten}$, was also shown.

$$
\begin{array}{rcl}
& 0\ 0\ 1\ 1 & = 3 \\
\times & 0\ 0\ 1\ 0 & = 2 \\
\hline
& 0\ 0\ 0\ 0 & \\
0\ 0\ 1\ 1 & & \\
\hline
0\ 0\ 1\ 1\ 0 & & = 6
\end{array}
$$

The computer does not actually function this way. The arithmetic steps are performed in a way that speeds up the computer's *internal* operation. It is beyond the scope of this book to explain the technical reasons for the computer's internal arrangement and exactly how this is most efficient for its tasks. However, the following steps are closer to explaining an actual operation. First, however, two explanations are necessary.

1. The number itself, such as 13 in binary, written as 1 1 0 1, is called the *magnitude bit*. A *sign bit* must be placed before it to show whether the number is positive or negative, plus or minus. Plus = 0; minus = 1.

	Sign bit	Magnitude bit
+13	0	1 1 0 1
−13	1	1 1 0 1

2. For any number there is some other number, called the *complement of the number,* that can be added to it to bring about the following result: a number that starts with 1 followed by a series of zeros equal to the digits of the first number. The second number is called *the 10's complement* of the first.

In binary, complements are simple. The empty spaces – zeros –

are filled; the filled spaces — ones — are emptied; the result is the complement of the first. For example, the binary complement of 7 is:

Binary 7 = 0 1 1 1
Its complement = 1 0 0 0

To bring a number back to its original form is called *recomplementing.*

To recomplement binary 7:

The complement of binary 7 = 1 0 0 0
binary 7 = 0 1 1 1 (recomplemented)

This is important because the computer subtracts by complementing negative numbers and doing addition instead of subtraction. The results are then recomplemented.

Problem. Subtract 12 from 7.

In ordinary arithmetic, it   7
would be done this way: −12
                                         ── 5 (answer)

This is how a computer sees the problem:

	Sign bit	Magnitude bit				
+ 7	0	0	1	1	1	
−12	1	0	0	1	1	(the complement of 12:
	1	1	0	1	0	1 1 0 0)

The sign bit is minus; the number must be recomplemented — *but not the sign bit.*

− 0 1 0 1 = −5

Multiplication. A computer does multiplication by getting partial sums, moving the digits to the right, and then continuing until it is through. You could do your multiplication in the same way. But while it is faster for a computer, it is not likely to be for you.

Problem. Multiply 5 × 7 (sign bits will be ignored).

$$5 = \quad 0\ 1\ 0\ 1$$
$$\times$$
$$7 = \quad 0\ 1\ 1\ 1$$

First partial product and first partial sum	$0\ 1\ 0\ 1$
Shift to right	$0\ 1\ 0\ 1$
Second partial product	$0\ 1\ 0\ 1$
Second partial sum	$0\ 1\ 1\ 1$
Shift to right	$0\ 1\ 1\ 1\ 1$
Third partial product	$0\ 1\ 0\ 1$
Third partial sum	$1\ 0\ 0\ 0\ 1\ 1$
Shift to right (not really necessary)	$1\ 0\ 0\ 0\ 1\ 1 = 35$

$$\updownarrow \qquad \updownarrow \quad \updownarrow$$
$$32 \qquad 2 \quad 1$$

One other multiplication process will be described — the multiplication of a positive and negative number (+6 × −2). The computer performs the following steps:

1. It examines the numbers to see if the answer will be plus or minus.

$$(+\times+=+)\ (-\times-=+)\ (+\times-=-)$$

2. A negative number is recomplemented.

3. The computer multiplies. If the product is positive, nothing else is necessary.

4. If the product is negative, it places a sign bit of 1 (−) before the number and gives the complement.

5. The answer is then recomplemented.

In this problem, −6 × −2, the computer performs as follows. It sees that the signs differ; the answer will, therefore, be negative. It recomplements the negative number (−2) by changing 1 (sign bit) 1 1 0 1 (the complement of 2) into 0 (sign bit) 0 0 1 0 (+2).

It then multiplies: 0   0 1 1 0 (+6)

by: 0   0 0 1 0 (+2)

The answer is: 0   1 1 0 0 (+12).

The computer remembers that the answer is negative, so that it complements the number to 1   0   0   1   1, the complement of 12.

The number is then recomplemented by the operator to −1 1 0 0, or −12.

If this appears to you to be a slow and involved method, remember this: In the time it took you to read and understand this, a computer could have multiplied thousands and thousands of numbers — negative, positive, or mixtures.

INDEX

Numbers in italics refer to illustrations.